Understanding Business

Quantitative Decision Making

John Harris and John Powell

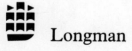
Longman

LONGMAN GROUP LIMITED
Longman House, Burnt Mill, Harlow,
Essex CM20 2JE, England
and Associated Companies throughout the World.

First published 1982
Second impression 1983

ISBN 0 582 35545 1 Pupils
ISBN 0 582 35552 4 Teachers

Set in Plantin 10/12 pt (Linotron 202)

Printed in Hong Kong by
Dai Nippon Printing Co. (H.K.) Ltd.

Contents

Acknowledgements

We are grateful to the following for permission to reproduce copyright material:

Lindley and Miller *Cambridge Elementary Statistical Tables* (Cambridge University Press) for Figure 17.1.

The Economist for tables on page 43.

Introduction to the Series

Once in a generation when an idea is coupled with resources, a completely new approach to a subject may be developed. So it has been over the last decade with the study of business behaviour for young adults, whether in schools or colleges, or in their management careers. The need for students to gain some real understanding of the nature and purpose of business activity has long been felt but there were no materials which would stimulate the minds of the academically gifted members of the age group.

These texts provide material for an examination of people's problems and behaviour within organisations. They discuss the nature of problems and explore concepts and principles that may be employed to aid their solution. Case materials are chosen from industrial and commercial organisations; from the private and the public sector; from non-profit-making institutions and the various colleges and schools with which students are automatically familiar. The material is as much to provide general understanding about industrial society and the workings of organisations as it is to help those who have already decided on a business or a professional career.

The approach of decision making has been used to draw together ideas and to give purpose, reality and challenge to the material. Any organisation is striving towards more or less closely defined objectives by deciding how to carry out and control its activity within constantly changing conditions. Ideas from the four functional areas of human behaviour, quantitative data, accounting and the economic environment are drawn together within a decision-making framework; the approach is then applied to different areas of business activity, particularly those of finance, marketing and production.

The level and approach has been shown to be suitable for sixth-formers, useful for BEC and TEC Higher courses and for students studying in their first-year degree programmes or a diploma in Management Studies. The series gives a rounded picture. However, each book stands complete in its own right.

All books have the same chapter format:
a chapter synopsis so that the purpose and pattern is clear;
a factual/explanatory text with case examples where applicable;
a participative work section to provide materials for learning, application and discussion.

These participative sections are an integral part of the whole text and allow the students to gain understanding by doing. They are usually divided into three parts. Firstly, some simple revision questions to enable the students to check their own basic understanding. Secondly, a series of exercises and case problems to test their application and to increase their knowledge of the area. Thirdly, a set of essay questions. Asterisks in the text highlight participative questions that have been designed to clarify those particular sections.

There is a teachers' booklet accompanying each student text which introduces the topic area, clarifies possible objectives, suggests approaches to the selected materials and provides solutions, where appropriate, to the participative work sections.

The philosophy, approach and materials now provide backing to an examination at 'A' level. The whole was developed through a project which was the brainchild of John Dancy, now Professor of Education, Exeter University. Without John Dancy's enthusiasm, energy, foresight and organisational skills, the Project would never have been formed. The Project has also gained great assistance through encouragement, ideas and finance from literally hundreds of educationalists, academics, businessmen and organisations. We thank all these. Without their help little could have been achieved. I hope it will not be thought invidious if I mention a few people and organisations: Professor Sir Austin Robinson who guided the setting up of the syllabus and examination; Leonard Wolfson and the Wolfson Foundation who provided the initial finances; Shell UK Limited who have done so much to pioneer the practical elements of the programmes; the University of Cambridge Local Examinations Syndicate for allowing the new subject, with a specially designed examination pattern, to be introduced; the Schools Council for advice and finance; the Longman Group Limited for their encouragement, understanding and helpfulness over publication; Marlborough College for giving their facilities to the Project team during the development period and the Institute of Education, London University, for agreeing to take this on post-August 1976; Jim Clifford and David Dyer for their work with the Project; the headmasters, teachers and students of 80 schools and colleges throughout the United Kingdom who pioneered the programme, used and commented on the ideas and materials; the many educational bodies who have spread these ideas.

Richard Barker
Series Editor
Formerly Project Director, 'A' Level Business Studies Project now renamed the Cambridge Business Studies Project

Preface

A Note to Readers

Take a look at your pocket calculator keys. If it is a fairly recent 'scientific' model, there is a reasonable chance that it has keys with symbols like σn, $\sigma_{(n-1)}$, $\bar{x}$ and VAR. When did you last use them? Do you know what uses they might have? Or does your calculator get used only for the four arithmetic functions – addition, subtraction, division and multiplication?

Whilst large organisations have well-established quantitative analysis sections, do line managers within them actually understand the implications of the figures on a computer printout? Do they understand the broad principles used in constructing the elegant computer programs, or do they blindly trust the 'whizz-kid' from the computer section?

An awareness of the potential of quantitative methods of analysis (*and* the limitations) is a valuable asset in any organisation. One need not necessarily know in detail how to analyse a given problem, but one *should* be aware that quantitative methods can help. Knowing that there is a problem, and where to turn for assistance, is half the battle.

This text is not intended to be a *Compleat Almanack of the Statistical Workes*, covering all likely situations. Rather it is an introductory survival kit. Our aim has been to produce a volume which introduces some of the more basic quantitative tools *without* assuming too high a mathematical ability. We hope that reading this book will give you the confidence to tackle problems *and* to delve into more specialist works. For this reason the book has been written from the point of view of the students' needs rather than as a compilation of statistical and other useful tools aimed at the specialist practitioner.

Some readers might occasionally be annoyed by the time we take to put a particular idea across. Please bear with us, as we want to encourage the less numerate to master the basics. We hope that we have avoided the use of phrases like, 'it is therefore obvious that . . .' or, 'clearly one can see that . . .'. One frequently can't!

Acknowledgements

This book is the result of suggestions, comments and exercises provided by many classroom teachers, students and others. Our particular thanks go to

David Dyer and Sue Anslow, who made many valuable suggestions in the early stages, and to Richard Barker, who has kept our noses to the grindstone, encouraged and cajoled us into getting all the various ideas onto paper.

Liz Rhea, our typist, deserves a medal. She has typed many drafts, each of which (we assured her) was 'definitely the last version'. She should be well-qualified to teach the area by now; after all, she has read several versions of the book over and over again!

If there are areas which you feel can be improved or clarified, we would be very pleased to have your comments. Needless to say, such errors as remain are our own.

Chapter 1

In the Beginning

Objective: *To show why one can no longer ignore numerate information in decisions.*

1.1 Being Numerate Matters

To be illiterate is to be a social outcast. Society places great value on the ability to create works of literature or drama. 'Men of letters' are accorded social acclaim. Schemes which help adults to read and write guarantee confidentiality, so great is the social stigma of illiteracy.

Yet to be innumerate carries no such mark. Indeed, on occasions, one might be forgiven for mistaking innumeracy for an essential social skill. 'I was *terrible* at maths when I was at school,' jokes the prize-day worthy, implying that it was no handicap. The audience sniggers its approval and understanding. Parents agonise over the fact that their child has a below-average reading age, but are 'understanding' when maths homework goes into the school bag unfinished. Somehow, society does not seem to value numeracy highly.

By numeracy, one means the ability to 'read' figures in the same way that one reads the written word. Numbers provide a convenient shorthand which can summarise and simplify patterns of activity. With changing technology, the need to 'read' figures is greater than ever before.

Until the last quarter of the twentieth century, society in advanced countries was essentially a paper-based one. That is, information was stored largely by means of the printed or written word. One had to go to the paper 'memory banks' in order to extract information, and the process of extraction was slow and labour intensive. Only large organisations, such as government, the armed forces and the big corporations had facilities for automated **information** storage and retrieval. Small and medium-sized organisations made do with the back of an envelope and latterly, a pocket calculator.

By 1980, the cheap, portable, computer was within the *financial* reach of even the one-man business. Pre-packaged **programs** covering a wide range of tasks are readily available, removing the need for a detailed knowledge of computer entrails. What *does* remain is the need to see where this cheap computer power can be used to advantage in the firm. Are computers within the *numer-*

ate reach of managers? Even the smaller **microcomputers** have a phenomenal capacity for recording data. Given the appropriate program instructions, that data can be assessed, analysed, rearranged and spewed forth for the decision maker to ponder.

The manager faced with all this potential information has three courses of action. Firstly, the 'immaculate conception' approach – 'Look Dick, I know what you said, but here it is in black and white on the printout. The computer can't be wrong.' Secondly, there's the 'ostrich' approach – 'Look, I don't care *what* that thing says. My mind's made up. I've got a *feeling*, and that's good enough for me.' Finally, there's the rather more practical approach of the realist – 'I don't know about you, but I'm pretty rusty on numbers. For all I know, the people who wrote the program could be having us on. Let's find out enough to see if we're having our legs pulled.'

This third approach is the one we hope to encourage in this book. Our aim is to give you a feel for some of the basic numerate tools. We cover the mechanics of calculation in many cases, but we also try to show *why* a particular approach is necessary. We hope that you will be able to see when quantitative analysis can improve decision making, or when someone else's findings are based on dubious analysis.

1.2 The Numerate Decision Maker

Let's lay a ghost at the outset. *People* take decisions, not computers or formulae. Numerate analysis of information may help to isolate key problems or to simplify complex situations. But one must always remember that some factors can never be fully quantified. The decision taker must balance both **quantitative** *and* **qualitative** aspects of a problem. Let's look at a few small examples to illustrate how quantitative analysis may be applied.

Domestica Homes Ltd   *The firm builds private housing and Bert Jones, the site foreman, has a problem. A wet week has put the building work behind schedule. Plumbers, electricians and plasterers are booked, yet the basic structure won't be ready for them unless something is done quickly. Bert's experience as a foreman will allow him to re-allocate work, but is his allocation the best possble? Or will the new allocation present further problems in the future? A small computer programmed for **network analysis** could show the short and long-term implications of reorganising the work, in terms of both time and cost. It allows Bert's decision making to be more informed.*

Hillside Engineering Ltd   *Elsie Harris operates a semi-automatic lathe which produces components in batches of ten thousand or so. She is responsible for checking that pieces are produced to specification. When should she stop the machine and ask a setter to re-set it? Her experience tells her that it is too late when bad work is being produced. Yet stop it too early, and the machine utilisation (and her pay) will fall. A control chart, rooted in probability theory, would help her to decide more positively. She could plot the results of each test, and only take action when they forewarn of problems ahead.*

Ginormous Enterprises Ltd   *Sir Adrian Jackson is Chief Executive of this large trans-national organisation. The Board is to decide on whether to expand into the West African market. He has plenty of information on sales performance, costings, market trends etc., but the decision clearly depends on far more than numerate factors. How stable is the government in Zamboanga? How reliable are the Zamboagan figures on economic and educational development? Are the firm's competitors eyeing the same market? Here, the decision maker can only make use of quantitative information up to a certain point. Thereafter, it is about judgement, intuition and 'feel', based on a long career in the industry.*

Porky Pies Ltd   *Jean Richards heads the new product section and is working on a turkey and ham pie. What is the optimum blend of ingredients which will satisfy the conflicting demands of legal standards, consumers' taste, supply constraints, processing capacity and the like? Here again, experience and intuition might produce a blend which is a reasonable solution. But is it the best? What happens if the price of turkey changes? What new blend should be substituted? Again, an analysis based on a mathematical model of the pie, and using the approach of operational research, may help Jean to find the optimum recipe under a given set of conditions.*

Midtown College   *At the start of the academic year, the Principal ran over the results of the summer examinations with the faculty heads. 'Let's look at the A levels, scoring five points for an A grade, four for a B and so on. Overall we've done better than before, with an average pass score of 3.72 as against our previous best of 3.69. The only slippage was in the Business Studies area, which fell from 3.39 to 3.36. I'll be asking for suggestions as to how we can improve this.' Was the Principal justified in assuming that standards had slipped? Had the overall standard really improved? Or were the results really no different from past years? Here is an example where figures are being abused. Figures are being quoted without any assessment of their statistical significance. Sampling theory would allow the Principal to assess the accuracy of his remarks.*

In each of these examples decisions *can* be made without reference to quantitative methods. The key point is whether the *quality* of the decisions reached could have been improved had numerate analysis been undertaken. Could the decision takers have been better informed?

1.3 Coming Shortly

A book of this size must be selective. No doubt you will find other books with more techniques per hundred pages. Our aim is to give you an introduction to this aspect of decisions, so that you can make more sense of rather more detailed texts which are readily available. Yet we also want you to have acquired a set of general skills which can be used in a wide variety of contexts.

Chapters 2, 3 and 4 look at the business of collecting and presenting the **data** for decisions, whilst Chapters 5 and 6 cover the general analysis that you are likely to carry out on most raw data.

Chapters 7 to 10 deal with improving one's certainty of observation using the various tools of **probability** and **sampling**.

Chapters 11 and 12 incorporate the perspective of time, through an examination of index numbers and forcasting. In the latter case, the blend of quantitative and qualitative analysis is very necessary.

Finally, Chapters 13 to 17 look at how the approach of **operational research** can help to unravel complex, multi-dimensional problems through the use of relatively simple **models**.

Most chapters contain a Work Section. The questions in Section A are intended to help you learn basic facts and concepts from the text, and might be used as the basis for revision work. Questions in Section B apply the ideas of the text to problems whilst Section C essays are intended to broaden your understanding and develop links to other areas.

In most chapters, we begin by introducing a typical problem. These have been set in a local authority context, partly to remind you that quantitative methods are not the preserve of the profit-making section of organisations. They can improve the effectiveness of all organisations, from the corner shop to the largest trans-national corporation.

And so to business . . .

Part I   The Raw Materials for Decisions
Chapter 2

Using Published Data Sources

Objectives: *To consider the problems and benefits of using published data sources, and to give examples of possible useful sources.*

Plan of the chapter:

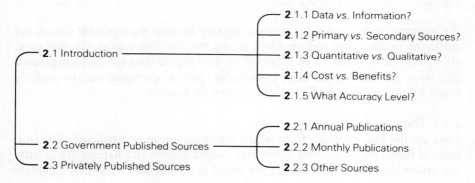

- 2.1 Introduction
  - **2**.1.1 Data *vs.* Information?
  - **2**.1.2 Primary *vs.* Secondary Sources?
  - **2**.1.3 Quantitative *vs.* Qualitative?
  - **2**.1.4 Cost *vs.* Benefits?
  - **2**.1.5 What Accuracy Level?
- 2.2 Government Published Sources
  - **2**.2.1 Annual Publications
  - **2**.2.2 Monthly Publications
  - **2**.2.3 Other Sources
- 2.3 Privately Published Sources

2.1 Introduction

In any decision-making situation we rely heavily on data and information to help us make up our minds. Quite often we have too much data in the sense that our minds cannot handle the bulk. In these circumstances decision makers have been heard to say, 'Don't confuse me with the facts.' A step-by-step approach to decision making can help to reduce the risk of confusion, and a possible model is shown in Fig. 2.1.

This model assumes a cycle of decision activities from problem diagnosis, through analysis, to choice and execution. The information-gathering stage is therefore a crucial one.

In this more logical approach, a manager may say, 'Give me information that I can use to evaluate the various alteratives.' This latter statement suggests that whilst there is always plenty of data available, this often does not produce

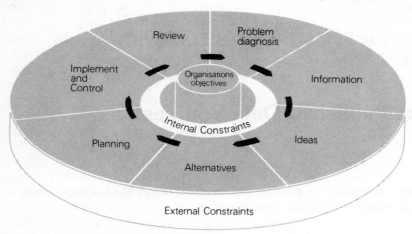

Fig. 2.1: A decision-making model

the information necessary for decision making because the available data is not pertinent to the particular problem facing the decision maker. In this case, either further data has to be collected or the original data has to be organised into ways that make them more presentable. Several questions may be usefully asked by the decision maker before starting an enquiry.

2.1.1 Data vs. Information?
Data are the raw materials from which information can be extracted. The millions of facts collected about individuals, organisations and nations are of little use unless they are processed and presented in a meaningful manner. Chapters 2–6 are concerned with this aspect of statistical enquiry.

2.1.2 Primary vs. Secondary Sources?
Primary sources are those which we research ourselves in order to get data 'from the horse's mouth'. Examples might include a street survey of TV viewing or a series of observations of the dimensions of products from a particular process.

Secondary sources are those from which we can extract part-processed data. Someone else has visited the horse's stable! Examples might include government statistical publications or a market research survey on the marmalade market in the UK.

This chapter concentrates on secondary sources, whilst Chapter 3 deals with primary data collection.

2.1.3 Quantitative vs. Qualitative?
'Phew, what a scorcher!' is a qualitative observation about a summer's day, whilst a thermometer reading of 28 °C is a quantitative measure. In this book, we concentrate on quantitative information, but we must *never* fall into the

trap of basing decisions solely on numerate information. Quantitative information may *appear* more accurate, and is certainly far easier to analyse and present. But never forget that the thermometer may be faulty! It is always worth remembering that numerate information may be accidentally or deliberately misleading. Some areas defy wholly objective, quantitative, measurement. Future events, employee morale or goodwill and national 'mood' would be impossible to quantify with any certainty.

2.1.4 Cost vs. Benefit?

A first step in collecting any data is to check whether the extra information so gained is worthwhile both in terms of cost and time. Clearly costs must be less than the monetary benefits gained from collecting extra data, but the consideration of the time involved is more often overlooked. For practising managers time is of the essence; it is not only important to get the right data, but the right data at the right time to make important decisions. The assessment of what may be useful data has to take place before any data are collected. This is not an easy task since, clearly, the decision to collect data has to be taken without knowing exactly what may be found. Clear formulation of the objectives of the overall decision will help, however.

2.1.5 What Accuracy Level?

Many figures are collected to inappropriate levels of accuracy or with unknown accuracies. Clearly too great an accuracy is a waste of time and expense; too little can invalidate the findings. Unknown accuracy can produce even more problems for it becomes far from clear what it can be used for.

The idea of accuracy is equally applicable to accuracy of definition. When using data on earnings one needs to examine exactly what is meant by 'weekly wages'. In addition, the definitions used in the data can change over time. An example of this would be the geographical coverage of an area, e.g. the County of Gloucestershire, before and after the reallocation of local boundaries. Also, definitions can sometimes be interpreted in a way not always intended. One example of this is the data relating to road accidents that involve personal injury. Thus, if one were attempting to work out the chances of being involved in a road collision, the odds would be seriously underestimated if one looked only at official statistics.

A further set of problems face the user of secondary information. The coverage of the original study may not have been the same as that required (e.g. a survey of house building may exclude council housing). The survey **sample** size may have been too small for reliable results to be drawn. Finally, the actual procedures in collecting the original data are beyond our control (e.g. a **questionnaire** may have been poorly worded or a sample incorrectly established).

Let us now look at potentially useful sources of secondary information. In developed countries, secondary data is provided by both public and private sectors.

2.2 Government Published Sources

Data published by the government tends to relate to the country as a whole, and to what may be termed the important indicators of society's well being. As such, the information is important to a very wide range of people.

There is a welter of well-presented, up-to-date, statistical data from this source. It is mostly published through Her Majesty's Stationery Office but naturally individual publications can be expensive (and are remarkably often out of print). Most researchers will rely on a good library for their initial work.

The first task will, as usual, be to choose from the sources available. In the first instance it would be a good idea to get hold of a copy of *Government Statistics – a Brief Guide to Sources*, which is published by HMSO and issued free of charge. For greater detail one would need to examine the *Guide to Official Statistics* which is an annual publication of the Central Statistical Office giving all the official publications under clearly classified divisions. It is designed to enable the public to make the maximum use of information gathered for government. Also *Statistical News* published quarterly by HMSO provides a summary of what government statisticians are doing, or intend to do in relation to particular industries or particular products. All these statistics can normally be taken as reliable but great care should be taken to see that the categories and definitions are suitable for your purpose.

Some important government publications are listed below. There are many others that are not listed because of constraints of space. It should be noted that each publication would normally have accompanying notes that provide greater detail than this text. These notes should be read very carefully before collecting and attempting to use the data.

★ 2.2.1 **Annual Publications**

(*a*) *The Annual Abstract of Statistics.* This is produced annually and provides figures for the last year along with tables covering the previous ten. It is far wider and more specific than the 'Blue Book' discussed below, and provides data on population, social conditions, labour, production, distribution and external trade, balance of payments, prices, national income and expenditure, home finance, banking, education, etc. It is precisely what its name implies – an abstract, but it is a good starting point for any investigation.

(*b*) *National Income and Expenditure.* This is a source publication for national account statistics which is published annually in September and often called the 'Blue Book'. It gives annual figures and estimates for the latest 22 years. It concentrates on national accounting data but also presents data on the institutional sector, personal and company sectors and an outline of transactions with overseas countries.

★ See Questions B1–B4

(c) *British Labour Statistics*. This is a yearbook put out by the Department of Employment. It presents, through tables and graphs, data on matters like earnings, vacancies, membership of trade unions, labour costs, etc. These may be in monthly figures or shown in annual tables or through 12-year tables; data is divided into industries, regions, etc.

(d) *Social Trends*. This is again published by the government's statistical service and is an annual. Through tables and a few charts (along with some useful comment) there is information on a wide variety of matters including health, income and wealth, housing, leisure interests, public safety and local authority expenditure.

(e) *Digest of United Kingdom Energy Statistics*. This is put out by the Department of Energy and provides comprehensive data relating to the fuel industries, including electricity, gas, coal and oil.

2.2.2 Monthly Publications

Apart from these annual sources there are a series of monthly publications. The most important of these are:

(a) *The Monthly Digest of Statistics*. This is small and easy to use and is of a general nature. However, it does show key statistics month by month and includes data concerning national income and expenditure, labour, industrial sectors (e.g. chemicals), external trade, wages and prices, and even the weather.

(b) *Department of Employment Gazette*. This covers the same type of ground as *British Labour Statistics* but appears far more regularly and has useful comment and articles around the newly available data.

(c) *Economic Trends*. There are three regular sections of tables and charts illustrating trends in the economy. The first shows the latest trends, giving all the most up-to-date statistical information which has become available during the month, together with a calendar of current economic events. The main section then gives the movement of pure economic indicators over the last five years. The third, general section, gives some longer term movements and provides additional comments and articles. If data from *Economic Trends* are used, then the reader should look at the annual supplement which provides notes and definitions and also gives long runs up to 30 years.

2.2.3 Other Sources

In addition to the general sources above, individual government departments often maintain further statistical information. Thus for a study of waste heat recovery units in the dairy industry, the Ministry of Agriculture, Fisheries and Food may have details. The free booklet *Government Statistics – A Brief Guide to Sources* contains a useful section on contact telephone numbers in individual departments. Official data covering wider geographical areas may be obtained from such sources as the United Nations or the European Commission.

2.3 **Privately Published Sources**

There are three main non-government sources of data. The first source is the company or organisation itself. Most organisations are required to produce an annual company report which will either be published (public companies) or available at Company House. Besides giving the basic accounting data as may be required by law, there is usually a considerable amount of additional information and comment from both the chairman and the directors. Read over a number of years, these can give considerable insight into the nature, developments and problems of a company. Most large companies also produce a considerable amount of internal data which is available. This may include papers on individual products, problems or developments, they may be data relating to general matters or detailed information about particular functional areas, but generally, this is only available for use within the company, as firms may operate in highly competitive markets.

The second source is from organisations such as trade unions or trade associations. They all offer different services to their members, and some may be of great value whilst others can present little in the way of data. Like companies, they may be unwilling to disclose information to 'outsiders'. Trade associations are listed in the *Directory of British Associations* whilst the TUC is a starting point for trade union information.

The third source is from companies which exist to provide information on a commercial basis. For this reason, their charges are often rather high! A number of companies offer market surveys, whilst others specialise in financial analyses (e.g. Nielsons or Jordans). Some periodicals also produce useful secondary information. *The Times 1000* gives details on company size and performance, whilst the Economist Intelligence Unit produces studies of particular fields. *Management Today*, *The Economist* and the *Financial Times* may also carry occasional survey results.

The advent of **electronic data processing** has made information even more accessible. The right information probably exists *somewhere*. The problem is knowing where to look!

Work Section

A. Revision Questions

A1 Distinguish between data and information.
A2 Distinguish between primary and secondary sources.
A3 Distinguish between qualitative and quantitative information.
A4 Why should investigators consider the cost vs. benefits of information?
A5 What do you understand by the term 'accuracy of data'?
A6 Name three annual government statistical publications.
A7 Name three monthly government statistical publications.
A8 What difficulties may arise when using secondary data?
A9 Why might you find it difficult to get detailed information on companies?
A10 What three main private sources are available?

B. Exercises/Case Studies

Questions 1–4 involve the use of *The Annual Abstract of Statistics*, which should be available at school or in your local library.

B1 Collect wage data for average weekly earnings of manual workers in manufacturing industries. Describe carefully exactly what your data shows.

B2 Use the *Annual Abstract* to find the Retail Price Index for the latest year available, and also find the price indices for the main groups that make up the Retail Price Index. Which group of items has risen (i) the most; and (ii) the least since the base year of the index?

B3 In the *Annual Abstract* find the table that deals with the number of pupils over the age of 16 in all schools. Draw up a table that shows the percentage number of boys, and separately, the percentage number of girls at school at the age of 16, 17 and 18 and over. Do this for the last ten years available in the *Annual Abstract*. Comment on your results.

B4 Indicate how you could attempt the same kind of tabulation as in B3 for the independent sector.

B5 If you were a trade union shop steward about the enter into negotiations for a pay rise, what national statistics would you find useful? Name the publications that you would use to find this data. Suggest other sources for any additional data – primary or secondary – that you would like to use.

B6 For each of the following members of a medium-sized firm in a highly competitive consumer durable market, in the UK, give one or two examples of national statistics which he might find of value. Give reasons for your answers.

(a) The personnel manager.
(b) The marketing manager.
(c) The production manager.

Source: Cambridge Examination Board A Level.

B7   A retailing company, which already has ten shops in various towns within an area of 50 miles square, now has the opportunity to purchase another shop in a different town in the same area. What information (quantitative and qualitative) should it seek before making the decision as to whether or not to expand?

Questions 8–11 could involve the use of any of the publications mentioned in the text. You should first decide to which publications you need to refer – most of them should be available in your local library – and find the appropriate tables. In each question give the precise source of your information.

B8   a. Draw up a table showing consumer expenditure at constant prices for the last ten years available.
     b. Find and tabulate the equivalent figures for food, drink and clothing. Compare the first and last year's figures.

B9   Find the size of the Public Sector borrowing requirement for each of the last ten years. What proportion of it was financed by (i) the banking sector; (ii) non-bank private sector; and (iii) overseas sector.

B10 Describe how the number of hours spent viewing television varies between (i) age groups and (ii) winter and summer. Suggest reasons for your findings.

B11 Compare data on the UK Gross Domestic Product in:
     a. *The Annual Abstract of Statistics*.
     b. Figures published by the OECD.
     Explain why the figures differ (use the explanatory notes to the tables).

C. Essay Questions

C1   Give reasons why individual organisations collect information.
C2   Discuss the role of information gathering in the sequence of decision making.
C3   Discuss sources likely to be of use:
     a. to a local authority.
     b. To a firm marketing consumer durable goods.

Chapter 3

Primary Data Collection

Objective: *To show the various factors and methods available to the researcher undertaking primary studies.*

Plan of the chapter:

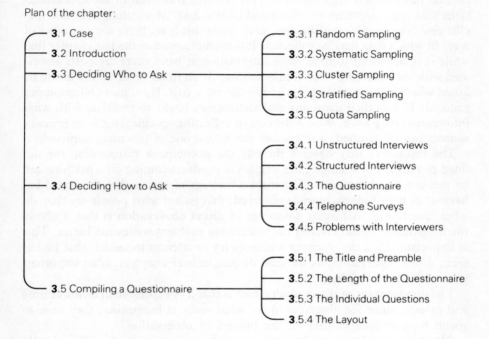

- 3.1 Case
- 3.2 Introduction
- 3.3 Deciding Who to Ask
  - 3.3.1 Random Sampling
  - 3.3.2 Systematic Sampling
  - 3.3.3 Cluster Sampling
  - 3.3.4 Stratified Sampling
  - 3.3.5 Quota Sampling
- 3.4 Deciding How to Ask
  - 3.4.1 Unstructured Interviews
  - 3.4.2 Structured Interviews
  - 3.4.3 The Questionnaire
  - 3.4.4 Telephone Surveys
  - 3.4.5 Problems with Interviewers
- 3.5 Compiling a Questionnaire
  - 3.5.1 The Title and Preamble
  - 3.5.2 The Length of the Questionnaire
  - 3.5.3 The Individual Questions
  - 3.5.4 The Layout

3.1 Case

Local transport has always been a problem in the outlying areas of what is now Merrion District. The spur railway line from Merrion was closed in 1969 under the Beeching Plan, and the local bus operators have been making a loss on their services in the area. The Council at Merrion have discussed the principle of providing a phone-in Minibus service for the country parts of the district.

A Statistics Department was established when local government reorganisation took place and the Council has asked it to determine the transport requirements of the 28,000 families in these outlying areas. The usual data gathered by the Council and the Statistics Department were found to be far too general for the needs of this very specific problem and thus some other form of obtaining information had to be devised.

3.2 Introduction

The previous chapter dealt largely with published data, in relation to which it was noted that such data rarely provided all the information needs of the decision maker. The same comment can be made for the data collected on a routine basis within organisations. This remains true even in those organisations that use computers to collect and collate data. More often than not specific problems require specific data, and, when this is so, there are a number of ways in which data may be collected. It was emphasised in the last chapter that while it is beneficial to have more information at hand there are costs associated with the gathering of such information. At all times the question has to be asked whether the extra benefits justify the extra cost. If so, data collection can proceed. If not, then managers and statisticians ought to make do with what information they have. Where the cost of collecting specific data from primary sources *can* be justified, a researcher can follow one of two main approaches.

The researcher may observe directly the phenomena surrounding the defined problem. For example, the weights of products coming off a machine can be measured and recorded. The main advantage of this is that the actual behaviour of men and machines is observed, that is, not what people *say* they do when questioned. A further advantage of **direct observation** is that it allows the investigator to understand the underlying problem somewhat better. This is important when the observer wishes to try to attempt to model what he has seen; direct observation, as we shall discuss in later chapters, is an important phase of model building.

The disadvantage of direct observation is that it is expensive in terms of time and money, since for observers to see what really is happening, they have to spend long periods of time in the process of observation.

Alternatively, the researcher may resort to *indirect* methods. This usually means asking people for their opinions (whether face to face or by a postal survey). The remainder of this chapter will be concerned with this last approach, using questionnaires to gain the desired data.

3.3 Deciding Who to Ask

In the Merrion transport study, there are 28,000 families whose opinions might be sought. We *could* ask all of them for their opinions, but it is unlikely that the cost in money and time would justify this. More likely, we would only ask a proportion of the families for their views. The statistical implications of sample size and sampling accuracy are covered in Chapter 10. In certain cases it may be either feasible or desirable to ask *all* possible respondents. One example is the 10-yearly annual census, last conducted on 5 April 1981. Another is seeking the views of everyone in a 10-person office.

★ A key step in sampling will be to ensure that the sample adequately reflects the whole **population** which *could* have been asked. There are various ways in which a sample may be drawn from a population.

3.3.1 Random Sampling

If a sample is drawn in such a way that each item selected has an equal chance of being drawn, then the sample is said to be a **random** one. (Other names used for a random sample are unrestricted or simple samples.)

When a population is homogeneous in regard to the characteristic in which we are interested, **random sampling** may be expected to give satisfactory results. By **homogeneous** is meant that there is no way of distinguishing between the items. When making a draw at raffle tickets or tombola this is the assumption made. Each person is represented in the draw by a ticket which is not different from any other ticket except with respect to the number on it. The tickets are then drawn from a hat or drum in a manner which is described as being random. Each ticket has an equal chance of being drawn.

Thus Merrion *could* put details of all 28,000 households on to identically sized slips of paper, pour them into a large drum, mix well, and then draw the required number of slips in order to select the households. An alternative may be to use tables of **random numbers**. Here, the annual electoral registers of the district might be the starting point (but even these will be out of date. Why?). The volume, page number and line of entry could be selected using a sequence of random numbers.

It is worth remembering that some apparently random information sources are distinctly non-random. Using the Merrion and District telephone directory to select households would automatically reject those without a telephone.

3.3.2 Systematic Sampling

This method was well known in the Roman Legions under the title of decimation. When a sample is obtained by drawing say, every tenth item on a list or in a file, the sample is said to be a systematic one. **Systematic sampling** was used, for example, in the 1961 population census when every tenth person was sent an extended questionnaire. Merrion might use the electoral register in this way.

★ See Question B1

No general statement can be made to the effect that more or less reliable results will emerge from systematic rather than random samples.

3.3.3 Cluster Sampling

Where there is a widely dispersed population it is sometimes advantageous from a cost point of view, to have a sampling unit. This is a basic entity and may be, for example, a firm, a block of flats, a geographic area etc. Within each sampling unit each individual may be interviewed. **Cluster sampling** is also known as **area sampling**. This will not be likely for the Merrion study.

3.3.4 Stratified Sampling

This is employed when the population has a number of characteristics which may vary. Thus the Merrion study might be **stratified** by ensuring that the sample contains representative proportions of high/middle/low income respondents, town/village/isolated dwelling families. A market research study might stratify by age, sex, and socio-economic status. Individuals within strata may possibly be chosen at random, resulting in a 'random stratified sample'.

3.3.5 Quota Sampling

In the types of samples mentioned above the interviewer plays no part in the selection of the people to be questioned. The interviewer is merely told to see and/or question a specified number of specifically named people. To obtain this interview, the investigator may have to call many times and even then the

---

Male: 1 1 1 1
Female: 1 1 1 1
              1 1 1 1
              1 1 1 1

Working Female: 1 1 1 1 1 1 1
Non-Working Female: 1 1 1 1 1 1 1

Age Distribution: Under 20: 1 1 1
                             20–30: 1 1 1 1
                             30–40: 1 1 1 1 1
                             40–60: 1 1 1
                             Above 60: 1 1

Socio-Economic Group: AB: 1 1
                                      C_1 1 1 1
                                      C_2 1 1 1 1 1 1
                                      DE   1 1 1 1 1 1

---

contact may not be established for a number of reasons – deaths, illnesses or holidays for example.

This process of calling back to try to make contact is time consuming and expensive. To economise on both of these a method of **quota sampling** has been evolved. This is the most frequently used method by market research organisations when seeking information about such things as products or political opinions.

In 'quota' sampling the interviewer is given a specified number of people to see. Instead of these being named – that is, see Jo Average of 35, Lilliput Avenue, Little Merrion – the interviewer would be asked to find the number of specified characteristics. Thus a typical 'quota' might be: 'Interview 20 people within the following specifications.'

The interviewer will then tick off which of these characteristics have been satisfied when conducting an interview. If conducted mid-morning in a shopping street on a Tuesday, the interviewer may find that some quotas are difficult to fill!

3.4 Deciding How to Ask

There are several methods open to the researcher and, once again, cost versus benefit will play a large part in the choice.

3.4.1 Unstructured Interviews
This may be done by asking questions in a fairly random way and letting the data surface whenever a relevant point arises in discussion. Such discussions are often tape recorded for later analysis. They have the advantage of allowing points to arise which may not have been thought of by a researcher in writing a more formal questionnaire. A variation is the group discussion, sometimes used in market research, which allows the group situation to stimulate ideas for discussion. It may also be used as a 'pre-test' session for questionnaire design.

3.4.2 Structured Interviews
Here, questions are predetermined and not asked randomly but in a pre-arranged manner. Structured interviews use the same kind of questionnaire technique that we will discuss below except that in an interview situation, the question can be more open-ended and discursive. The advantage of a structured interview over the less formal one described above, is that it allows easier comparison of answers between people and is usually capable of being tabulated more easily for further analysis. Note that the interviewer both asks the questions and records the answers. Where a number of possible answers might be given, the interviewer may show the respondent a card whilst asking, 'Which of these most closely agrees with your own views?' Many market research organisations use this form of interviewing.

3.4.3 The Questionnaire

These are usually distributed for collection some time later. Some might be sent via the post and so provide for return postage. Respondents reply to questions by ticking boxes, or by writing at greater length. Section 3.5 looks at questionnaire design in more detail.

At this stage we should note that the method has some broad advantages and disadvantages. The main advantage is that the apparent cost is low compared with other methods since there is no need to train interviewers and the costs of posting are small compared with the travelling costs of interviewers when they try to establish contact with their quota. Moreover, the postal questionnaire avoids interviewer bias and allows the respondent to give a considered reply rather than an instantaneous reply to the questions posed.

There are a number of disadvantages associated with the postal questionnaire. First, since the response rate is usually low, the real costs of obtaining information may be quite high. More questionnaires have to be sent out than is really necessary if everyone replied. In addition only simple questions may be asked and there is no way of checking that the answers given are those of a person whose opinion is sought.

3.4.4 Telephone Surveys

This method of obtaining information is gaining in popularity. There are obvious advantages since in general terms it lies between the cold, clinical, questionnaire and the face-to-face personal interview. It also tends to lie between the two from a cost point of view.

It used to be thought that telephone interviews would necessarily be biased because not everyone owns a telephone. This is less true than it used to be especially in well developed countries, but care would need to be exercised to establish that the sample taken was as representative as possible.

3.4.5 Problems with Interviewers

Unstructured and structured interviews may introduce **bias** into the results unless care is taken in the selection and training of an interviewer. Indeed in some cases, it may be virtually impossible to avoid bias (e.g. a survey of racial attitudes conducted in a mixed race area with a white middle-class interviewer).

Interviewer training aims to reduce bias by improving interpersonal skills and establishing a neutral stance.

Interpersonal skills include the ability to quickly establish a good working relationship with a respondent, including discussions on content, purpose and confidentiality; the ability to listen to respondents, helping but not directing; the ability to record accurately and concisely what has been said.

Neutrality involves ensuring that respondents give their *own* replies. Bias can easily slip into interviews, via such things as facial expressions, accent or tone of voice. All can reveal the interviewer's own prejudices. Less than professional interviewers may also take 'short cuts' – incorrectly completing a quota sample, rephrasing questions so as to change their validity and so on. Results from such interviewers will invalidate the statistical soundness of an enquiry at great cost (if they are spotted, that is).

3.5 Compiling a Questionnaire

★ Most questionnaire forms handle two types of question, *Classification* and *Subject Matter*. Classification data divides the population up into basic categories for the subsequent analysis. Depending on the purpose of the survey, the questionnaire might have questions about the age, sex and income group or occupation of the respondent. Only essential data should be sought in this section, and irrelevant questions must be avoided at all costs. If the subsequent subject matter questions are to be of a personal or confidential nature, respondents may be more willing to disclose information if they have given little to identify themselves in the classification.

The subject matter section deals with the theme of the questionnaire, and is therefore the area to which most attention will be given. There are four key factors in the design of a questionnaire form.

3.5.1 The Title and Preamble

There are very few occasions on which completion of a questionnaire, or the giving of information to an interviewer, is compulsory (the Census of Production and the Census of Population are perhaps the two most common examples of such surveys). The respondents' participation is therefore quite voluntary, and considerable skill is required to persuade people to take part.

It helps to state the purpose of the survey in the opening paragraph of the questionnaire form. If the person taking part in the survey can be encouraged to answer, in the knowledge that his replies do have some importance, genuine reactions are likely to be forthcoming. Whenever the post is used, make sure that stamped addressed envelopes are supplied for the respondent. The respondent should not feel that they are put to any more inconvenience or expense on your behalf than is absolutely necessary.

3.5.2 The Length of the Questionnaire

Ask only a minimum number of questions. Response rates increase when the questionnaire is short, and time and money can be saved in collection and collation.

3.5.3 The Individual Questions

The questions appearing on the form should:
a. not be ambiguous but as precise as possible.
b. be easy to understand, employing no technical jargon.

★ See Question B2

c. not lead the reader towards a particular answer by simple suggestion or emotional wording.

d. not offend the potential respondent.

e. not ask for any calculation, or rely on the respondent's memory more than is absolutely necessary.

f. be set in a way which is easy to complete, suitable for tabulation and really helpful with the decision in hand.

★ g. not ask more than one question each time.

h. state any units which may be required or use the yes/no/don't know alternatives.

To assess the degree that people may like or dislike particular things 'rating scales' can be introduced. For example, if one were trying to assess the relative merits of different types of tea, it might be more useful to ask of each tea the degree to which each respondent likes or dislikes the tea. That is instead of asking, 'Did you like tea X?' YES/NO, it would be more accurate to measure strength of reaction by a range of questions such as:

I like it very much.

I quite like it.

I neither like nor dislike it.

I dislike it slightly.

I did not like it at all.

Commonly, scores are given to these responses such as $+2$, $+1$, 0, -1, -2 for the five shown above. Such scores can be formed into a frequency distribution and further statistical analysis may be undertaken on the data.

Some questionnaires may used a tick box to indicate flavour of response. The scale is usually a 5 or 7 point one, with suitable words or phrases at each end of the line of boxes. For example, if we were trying to assess the strength of management in a factory some information may be gained by using the scale below:

Weak ☐☐☐☐☐☐☐ Strong

3.5.4 The Layout

The layout of the form should make the whole questionnaire as clear as possible. Whenever possible, maintain a flow of questions through the questionnaire. Sufficient space must be left for replies. Too little space may mean that all the relevant detail that a respondent wishes to put down on the form cannot be included. Conversely, too much space may invite unnecessary detail which has to be sorted out later by the analysts. The layout should also be one which assists in the analysis of results.

Conducting a survey by questionnaire, while being less expensive than inter-

---

★ See Question B4

views, is still going to cost money. It is important that precautions are taken to assure the success of the survey by carrying out a Pilot Project. Conditions for this should be as near as possible those of the actual survey. A Pilot Project is a vital stage in the survey process as from this the major problems are likely to be identified. It is an essential for an inexperienced survey organisation.

Work Section

A. Revision Questions

A1 Distinguish between direct and indirect methods of observation.

A2 What is a sample?

A3 What is the key feature of a random sample?

A4 Why may systematic or cluster sampling be used in preference to random sampling?

A5 What is the main aim of stratified sampling?

A6 What are the principal advantages and disadvantages of using questionnaires as a survey tool?

A7 What features would one look for in an interviewer?

A8 Questionnaires are divided into two main sections. What are they?

A9 What factors should be borne in mind when framing questions in a questionnaire?

A10 Why is a Pilot Project survey advisable?

B. Exercises/Case Studies

B1 Suppose you were asked to conduct a survey on the use of catering facilities in your own institution. How would you select your sample?

B2 Design a questionnaire that you feel will show young people's opinions on TV programmes.

B3 Now try your questionnaire from B2 on a small group sample and refine it in the light of group discussion.

B4 Comment on the wording and layout of each question set below. Suggest improvements in a precise form.

Sales of Petrol

This questionnaire has been devised by the British Petroleum Bureau. It is hoped to find out more of the consumers requirements when purchasing petrol. All information given will be treated confidentially.

1. Name _____

2. Sex   Male/Female

3. Indicate your marital status _____

4. How old are you?   Under 21

                                  21–40

                                  41–60

                                  Over 60

5. *Do you purchase most of the petrol or does your wife* _____

6. *How much petrol did you purchase last year?*   *Under 100 gallons*
   100–199 gallons
   200–299 gallons
   300 gallons or over.

7. *What is your car's engine capacity?* _____

8. *In choosing where you purchase your petrol, what effect have pump prices?*
   _____

9. *State, as fully as you can, why you purchase one brand of petrol rather than another* _____

10. *Are you in favour of even more free trading stamps with each purchase?   Yes/No.*

11. *Do you purchase petrol, whilst on business trips, so that you may be able to gain personal advantage from trading stamps, cut-price goods, etc.?   Yes/No*

12. *Do you motor a large or small mileage each year?* _____
    _____

We should be grateful if you could return this as soon as possible.
Thank you for your help.

British Petroleum Bureau

B5   *The Merrion Study*

As a result of considering the relevant factors, it was decided that the Merrion study should be based on a sample of 500 households drawn randomly from the electoral register. Forms would be distributed by post, and collection would be made by Council staff (who could help in cases of difficulty).

Merrion District Council

Highways Committee

Dear Householder,

We are trying to improve Public Transport in the Country areas of the District. Your answers in this questionnaire will help us to provide a better service.

You have been selected from the current Electoral Register, and we would be grateful if you would answer the questions below. All replies will be treated in confidence.

A week after you receive this form, one of the Council's Staff will call on you to collect the card and will be pleased to answer any questions that you have about filling in the form. Thank you for your help with this survey.

J. C. Reindorp
(Chairman)

Local transport survey

1. *Address:* _____
2. *How many people over the age of 15 normally live here?* _____
3. *How many children under the age of 16 normally live here?* _____
4. *For each adult member of the household (16 and over) please answer the questions in the table below for any journeys made to or from work each day.*

Normal Days★	*Journey to:*	*Via: by Car, Bus, etc?*	*Time of dept from home*	*Time of dept from work*
M T W Th Fr S S				
M T W Th Fr S S				
M R W Th Fr S S				
M T W Th Fr S S				
M T W Th Fr S S				

★ *Please tick days normally travel.*

Additional information _____

5. *For each person in full time education, please list the school or college, and the means of transport and travel times.*

School or College	*Means of transport*	*Time of dept from home*	*Time of dept from school/college*

Additional information _____

6. *For all other journeys (not to work or school/college) how many times does each member of the family travel to each of the following places in the course of one month?*

No.	*Merrion*	*Barlow*	*Prestock*	*Overton*

Additional information _____

7. Which of the following shopping precincts do you use for the main weekly shopping? (Please tick one or more as appropriate)

    1. Merrion (St. Pauls) _____
    2. Merrion (Cartwell) _____
    3. Barlow (Haven) _____
    4. Barlow (Chesterton) _____
    5. Prestock _____
    6. Overton _____

8. Which of the following methods of transport do you use to travel to the shopping centre? (Please tick one or more)
    1. Motor car _____
    2. Bicycle _____
    3. Motor Cycle _____
    4. On foot _____
    5. Bus _____
    6. Other means (please indicate) _____

9. How many motor cars are owned by people resident at this address? _____
10. Is there a telephone installed at this address? _____

Comment on the Merrion questionnaire and the proposed methods of sampling.

C. Essay Questions

C1 Discuss, with examples, situations in which it would be appropriate to use:
    a. Quota sampling.
    b. Random sampling.
    c. 100 per cent population sampling.
C2 'Sampling errors are usually associated with the methods of selecting the sample.' Do you agree?
C3 Discuss the sampling considerations likely to be found in:
    a. A traffic census.
    b. Sales of school books.
    c. Attitudes towards capital punishment.
    d. Recognition of a brand name used in advertising.

Chapter 4

The Presentation of Data

Objective: *To show how data can be presented in a form suitable for analysis by decision makers.*

Plan of the chapter:

- **4**.1 Case
- **4**.2 Introduction
- **4**.3 Tabulation
- **4**.4 Graphical Presentation
  - **4**.4.1 Choice of Axes
  - **4**.4.2 The Lorenz Curve
- **4**.5 Diagrammatic Presentation
  - **4**.5.1 Pie Charts
  - **4**.5.2 Bar Charts
  - **4**.5.3 Plots of Frequency Distribution

4.1 Case

Merrion's Statistics Department is conscious of the fact that in order to provide a useful service, data collected must be presented in useful ways. A frequent charge levelled at the Council is that it keeps a lot of useless data. To overcome some of these complaints, the Department's head has decided to pay more attention to the way in which data is to be presented. This will inevitably mean finding out more about the uses to which the data will be put as well as the skills of the users.

4.2 Introduction

The last two chapters have discussed how data may be collected. Successful use and interpretation depends on data being presented in a manner which makes it easy for the user to understand whilst, at the same time, maintaining as much accuracy and freedom from bias as possible. It is also important to allow the user to return to the source as and when required.

We are all familiar with the narrative approach of television, newspapers and books. In a typical news report, one might hear something like the following. 'Trade figures out today showed a surplus of £900 million in March. Imports were at a low level of £2,142 million as a result of the recession here at home, which is well down from their peak of £3,420 million only two years ago. On the export side, almost £300 million came from oil sales, itself doubled over the past year and a half.'

How much of a picture did you get? On screen, the commentary was supported by coloured graphs and blocks. But did you get the *real* picture? In all but the simplest cases, the human mind shuts out too much information – as students know only too well! The statistician needs to summarise the information available in such a way that the user can grasp clearly and concisely the most important features. In general, there are three main ways of achieving this end, using tabulation, graphs and diagrams. Let us now look at each in more detail.

4.3 Tabulation

Tables are one of the commonest forms of data presentation. In principle, **tabulation** is the technique of arranging data in labelled rows and columns, allowing rapid assessment and comprehension of the material.

There are no rules for tabulating data, but certain commonsense principles should be followed to obtain the greatest effect from statistical information. The choice of a particular tabular format must inevitably depend on the material being handled, but the overriding question must always be, 'What is the table trying to achieve?'.

Is it being constructed

a. to present crude, unprocessed information in an orderly fashion?
★ b. to summarise information?
c. to indicate trends or patterns in statistics?
d. to make data available for subsequent analysis? (for example, government transport statistics, which are to be used by local authority planners).

Each of these will require different forms of tabulation if the central ideas are to be put across quickly.

Example: Small Engineering Company Ltd is a manufacturer of mechanical fasteners for the packaging trade. It has a share capital, fully paid up, of £12,000 in £1 Ordinary shares. This was increased from £10,000 in 1979. The summary of financial data for the seven-year period 1976–82 is given in Fig. 4.1.

★ See Question B10

Year	Sales (£)	Gross profits (£)	Overheads (£)	Dividends p/share
1976	52,100	18,060	11,430	6.4
1977	56,300	19,130	12,590	6.6
1978	53,100	17,280	13,280	6.9
1979	62,560	21,240	15,410	7.2
1980	69,130	24,360	18,300	7.6
1981	71,810	30,210	22,360	8.0
1982	78,300	33,450	23,100	8.5

Fig. 4.1: Company performance 1976–82

How can this best be presented in tabular form:
a. to allow the Board to assess the company's return on capital?
b. to assist a potential investor contemplating a small investment in the company?
c. to enable the company's cost accountant to examine the overheads?

Return on Capital
The relevant information that the Board will want to have summarised will be the net profit (derived from the gross profit and overheads), capital employed, and net profit expressed as a fraction of the capital. This is shown in Fig. 4.2 with the final column showing the return (post-tax profit over share capital).

Financial Performance 1976–82

Year	Gross profit (£)	Overheads (£)	Net profit (£)	Post-tax profit (£)	Share capital (£)	Return (%)
1976	18,060	11,430	6,630	3,978	10,000	39.78
1977	19,130	12,590	6,540	3,924	10,000	39.24
1978	17,280	13,280	4,000	2,400	10,000	24.00
1979	21,240	15,410	5,830	3,498	12,000	29.15
1980	24,360	18,300	6,060	3,636	12,000	30.30
1981	30,210	22,360	7,850	4,710	12,000	39.25
1982	33,450	23,100	10,350	6,210	12,000	51.75

Source: *Company Accounts*

Fig. 4.2: Summary of firm for the Board

The Investment Assessment
To the potential investor in the company, the key factors are going to be the profit per share, dividend per share and hence the number of times the dividend has been covered in each of the years. For the inexperienced investor, it may be best to highlight the earnings (distributed and undistributed) whereas for the experienced reader only the dividend and cover need be given.

Investment Performance 1976–82

Year	Net profit	Dividend	Earnings/ share	Dividend/ share	Dividend cover
	(£)	(£)	(p)	(p)	(times)
1976	6,630	640	66.3	6.4	10.4
1977	6,540	660	65.4	6.6	9.9
1978	4,000	690	40.0	6.9	5.8
1979[1]	5,830	864	48.6	7.2	6.8
1980	6,060	912	50.5	7.6	6.6
1981	7,850	960	65.4	8.0	8.2
1982	10,350	1,020	86.3	8.5	10.1

[1] *Issued share capital increased from 10,000 × £1 to 12,000 × £1 shares*
Source: *Company Accounts*

Fig. 4.3: Financial summary of firm

The Accountant's Cost Analysis
You can now draw up a table suitable for the cost accountant who will be concerned with the fraction of the income which is taken up by overhead expenses. Capital will not be a critical factor and its inclusion will not be required.

★ These three applications illustrate the ways in which the same basic information may be used for slightly different purposes. In each case an attempt has been made to exclude excessive information from the table. This should always be the aim of a statistician – as should the aim to produce all the relevant information needed for analysis. The ability to draw up a table which meets a specific requirement is developed with practice and knowledge of the interpretative skills and purpose of the reader. In each case the table should be:
a. labelled clearly and accurately; b. the units clearly marked in all cases; c. the full source of the data recorded. This latter is particularly important in tables which are often used by specialists, along with further information, to analyse complex problems.

4.4 Graphical Presentation

Tables alone may lack sharp visual impact, and may be better used in conjunction with **graphs**. The graph may help the mind to grasp spatial relationships much more quickly than blocks of numbers. Figure 4.4 below shows the essential features of a graph.

★ See Question B4

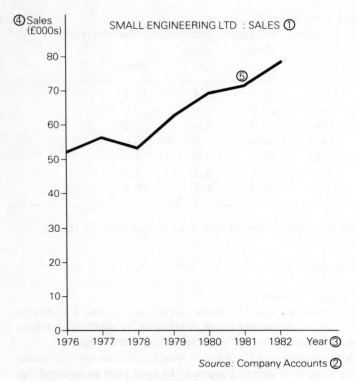

Fig. 4.4: A graphical plot of Small Engineering's sales

The plot shows:
- A clear title ① and source ② (as with tabulation).
- The horizontal (or *x*) axis ③ which is used for, and marked as the independent variable, i.e. the cause of change, in this case time.
- The vertical (or *y*) axis ④ used for the dependent variable, i.e. the effect of changes caused by the *x* axis variable.
- The points joined together. Here they are joined by straight lines since the sales values only occur for each year. (Thus sales and time are said to be **discrete variables**.) A smooth curve is drawn when there are an infinite (or very large) number of possible values (e.g. the heights of adult females in Sweden), in which case height is a **continuous variable**.

Let us now consider a few further points on graph construction.

4.4.1 Choice of Axes
The **axes** intersect at right angles, but need not be restricted to the 'L' shape of Fig. 4.4. It may be necessary to show negative as well as positive values as shown below in Fig. 4.5.

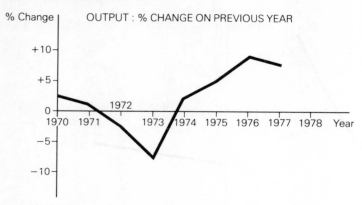

Fig. 4.5: Plot with positive and negative scales

Both Fig. 4.4 and Fig. 4.5 are showing *absolute* changes in one variable compared to another. For this reason they used **arithmetic scales**. This means that equal distances on each separate axis will correspond to equal changes in the quantity being measured.

In some statistics, however, the need to show *relative* change is more important than the absolute amount. Here a **logarithmic scale** may be more appropriate. (Where both axes are logarithmic, the graph is called a '**log-log**' plot. Where one is logarithmic and one arithmetic, it is termed a '**semi-log**' plot.) Equal distances along a logarithmic scale correspond to equal *relative* changes.

Consider the example of investing £100 at an annual compound rate of interest of 10 per cent. For the first ten years, one's investment will have grown to the following sums:

Year	*1*	*2*	*3*	*4*	*5*	*6*	*7*	*8*	*9*	*10*
Amount(£)	*100*	*110*	*121*	*133*	*146*	*161*	*177*	*195*	*214*	*236*

Plotted arithmetically (Fig. 4.6(a)) one appreciates the quickening absolute growth. Plotted on a semi-log scale (Fig. 4.6(b)) one can see the underlying relative growth, in this case a constant 10 per cent p.a.
Note that the origin on the log axis can never be zero. Here, equal divisions imply a ten-fold increase.

Semi-log and log-log graph paper can be purchased, but one can always use ordinary graph paper, plotting the logarithm of the number. Hence $\log_{10}$ of $100 = 2.0$, $\log_{10}$ of $110 = 2.04$ etc.

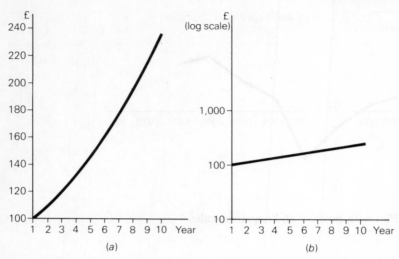

Fig. 4.6: Graphical plots (a) Using arithmetic scale to show *absolute* growth
(b) Using a logarithmic scale to show *rate* of growth

4.4.2 The Lorenz Curve
The form of graph known as the **Lorenz Curve** is particularly useful if one
wishes to show inequalities of distribution (e.g. of income, of quality, or of
labour). Each axis shows a cumulative percentage scale running from 0 per
cent to 100 per cent.

*As an example, consider the industrial disputes record of an industrial sector, as a
function of the size of firms.*

No. of employees	Total no. of stoppages	Total no. of man-days lost
1–10	*1,200*	*125,000*
11–100	*453*	*161,000*
101–1,000	*402*	*282,000*
1001–10,000	*592*	*1,250,000*
Over 10,000	*24*	*2,625,000*
	2,671	*4,443,000*

*We can now calculate the cumulative percentage of stoppages and man-days lost
for each category.*

★ See Question B6

No. of employees	No. of stoppages			No of man-days lost		
	No.	%	Cum. %	No.	%	Cum. %
1–10	*1,200*	*44.9*	*44.9*	*125,000*	*2.8*	*2.82*
11–100	*453*	*17.0*	*61.9*	*161,000*	*3.6*	*6.4*
101–1,000	*402*	*15.1*	*77.0*	*282,000*	*6.4*	*12.8*
1001–10,000	*592*	*22.2*	*99.2*	*1,250,000*	*28.1*	*40.0*
Over 10,000	*24*	*0.8*	*100.0*	*2,625,000*	*59.1*	*100.0*
	2,671	*100.0*		*4,443,000*		

Plotting the respective cumulative percentage values on the scales will show how the stoppages are distributed, as shown in Fig. 4.7.

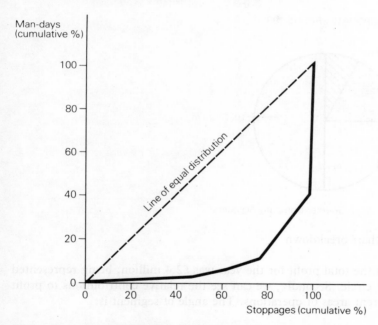

Fig. 4.7: Lorenz curve for industrial stoppages

The curve shows dramatically that relatively few stoppages account for the vast majority of man-days. Indeed just over 60 per cent of all stoppages resulted in 6 per cent of man-days lost. Thus only a minority of stoppages were prolonged, concentrated in the large firms in the industry.

Had stoppages and days lost been distributed evenly through all firms, the distribution would have followed the dotted line in Fig. 4.7. Deviation from this line shows the extent to which concentration has occurred.

4.5 Diagrammatic Presentation

The main purpose of this approach is to give quick visual impact in support of an argument rather than to allow detailed analysis. The **diagrams** which open most chapters of this book are simple examples of this approach. The most widely used forms of diagrammatic presentation are the **pie chart** and the various forms of **bar chart**. Because they rely mainly on visual impact, great care needs to be taken to see that they do not confuse, or are not designed to mislead.

★ ### 4.5.1 Pie Charts
The name aptly describes this form of presentation. A whole is sub-divided into its various parts in the same way as a pie is served in segments. From the diagram below, what can be deduced about a firm's profit breakdown in a given year?

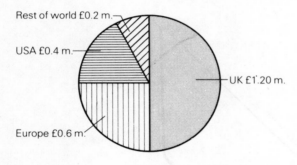

CORPORATE PROFITS 1982

Source: Company Accounts

Fig. 4.8: Pie chart breakdown

Firstly, that the total profit for the year was £2.4 million, being represented by 360° of the circle. Secondly, we can see the relative contributions to profit from the different areas of operations. The angle of segment is:

$$\frac{\text{Sub-total}}{\text{Grand total}} \times 360°$$

and so for the USA with profits of £0.40 million, the angle is

$$\frac{£0.40 \text{ m.}}{£2.40 \text{ m.}} \times 360° = \underline{60°}$$

★ ## See Questions B2–B5

No attempt is made to allow accurate numerical estimation. We could certainly not read the figures off to the nearest thousand.

In the case of a single pie chart, the size of the circle has no significance. However, if two sets of similar statistics, where a different total was involved, are being compared, the *area* of the circles should be in proportion to each of the total figures.

Thus, if the profit increased next year to £3.0 million, the *areas* would have to be shown in the proportion

Year 1: Year 2 = £2.4 m.: £3.0 m. = 1: 1.25.

The *diameters* of the circles would therefore have to be in the proportion 1: √1.25, or approximately 1:1.12. Periodicals such as *The Economist* often contain pie charts to give visual impact to text.

★ 4.5.2 Bar Charts

A bar chart has many of the same virtues as a pie chart. It probably allows a greater simple comparison between the areas of different sectors of a total whilst it can be used to portray a series of magnitudes (and sectors within these) for a period with greater clarity.

The height of the bar (or length when bar is horizontal) is directly proportional to the magnitude of the data that it represents. The width of the bar has no significance.

Recalling the example of Small Engineering Co. Ltd (Section **4.3**), the gross profits might be presented as a bar chart, as shown in Fig. **4.9** below.

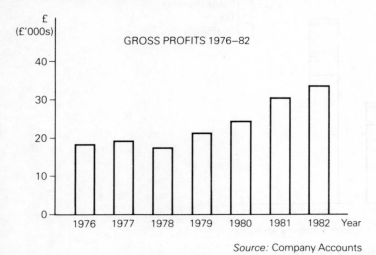

Source: Company Accounts

Fig. 4.9: Bar chart of profits

★ See Questions B3 and B5

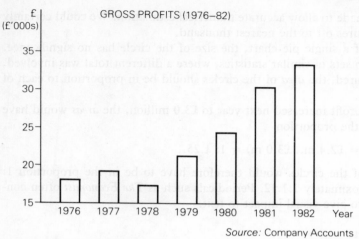

Source: Company Accounts

Fig. 4.10: Deception through scaling

Deception through the use of scales is illustrated in Fig. 4.10. The deception may be accidental rather than deliberate, but it is still a misleading plot.

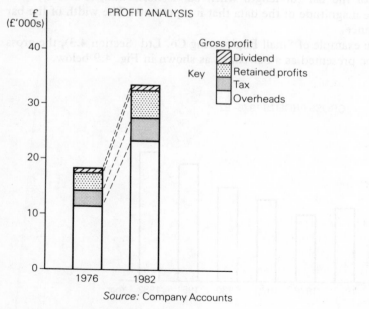

Source: Company Accounts

Fig. 4.11: Segmented bar chart

Bars may be segmented vertically to show breakdowns in a manner similar to the pie chart, as Fig. 4.11 illustrates.

Whilst the general magnitudes of the division should now be clear, the exact totals may be difficult to read off from the scale. The approach works best when there are only a small number of divisions.

An alternative method of presentation is to have parallel bars for each period, as in Fig. 4.12.

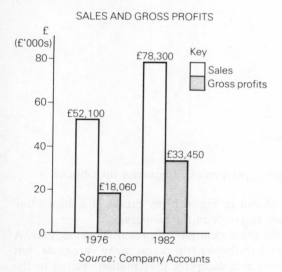

Fig. 4.12: Using parallel bars for clarity

4.5.3 Plots of Frequency Distribution

In many areas of statistical enquiry, the results may be produced in the form of a frequency distribution. Whilst the next chapter looks at these in more detail, let us briefly consider presentation methods which may be used. The key requirement is to show how frequently a given event or observation occurs.

As an example, consider the researcher who was looking at the number of defective nails per box of 100. The results obtained from 20 boxes were:

No. of defectives found/box 0 1 2 3 4
No. of boxes   5 7 4 3 1

The **histogram** is a form of bar chart in which the area of the rectangle is used to designate the magnitude of the variable being considered (as opposed to the height in the bar charts of Section **4.5.2**).

In practice, histograms are often drawn on the basis of equal length of base for the rectangles for each value and, if this is so, the height of the rectangle may be taken as a measure of the variable. Another difference between a bar chart and a histogram is that in the latter the rectangles are drawn so that they are touching each other.

Histograms are often used by statisticians when raw data have been classified and a visual presentation is thought appropriate.

Figure 4.13 shows a histogram plot of the data.

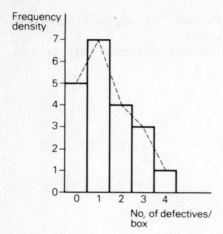

Fig. 4.13: Histogram and frequency polygon of a frequency distribution

A **frequency polygon** is also shown in Fig. 4.13 by means of a dotted line drawn between the centre of each rectangle in the histogram.

This chapter has only given the main examples of presentation methods. A look at newspapers, television and textbooks will reveal many variations, but the underlying principles of clear, non-deceptive presentation, suited to the needs of the recipient, remain.

Work Section

A. Revision Questions

A1 Why should statisticians bother to present their results with care?

A2 What factors should you consider when constructing a table.

A3 What factors should you consider when producing a graph?

A4 When should points on a graph be joined a. by straight lines; b. by a smooth curve?

A5 Distinguish between arithmetic and logarithmic graph axes.

A6 What is the aim of the Lorenz curve?

A7 The profits of a company for two years are to be presented in the form of pie charts. How should they be drawn?

A8 In a bar chart, what is the height of a bar proportional to?

A9 Distinguish between a histogram and a simple bar chart.

A10 What is a frequency polygon?

B. Exercises/Case Studies

B1 Taking the information from the example in Section **4.3**, produce a table suitable for the cost accountant to analyse the company's overheads.

B2 A pie chart is to represent total sales revenue of £60 m. What amount of revenue is represented on that pie chart by 33°? What angle would be needed to isolate £18 m? A second comparable chart is to show sales of £180 m. What will be the ratio of the radii of the two circles?

B3 Pipe Rollers Ltd had a turnover in 1976 of £250 m. worldwide, of which £50 m. was in the UK, £100 m. was from the USA and the remainder was taken elsewhere. Construct as many different types of bar chart as possible to represent this information tidily and unambiguously.

B4 Read the following passage about the UK national economy, and draw up a suitable table to contain the statistical data.

> *Public expenditure on goods and services has increased in monetary terms every year since 1949, when the level was £2,040 millions. By 1954, the figure had risen to £3,190 millions; £4,001 millions by 1959, and £5,510 by 1964. In 1969, the expenditure by the Public Sector had risen to £8,118 millions. Over the same period, the total expenditure at market prices rose from £11,230 millions in 1949 to £17,884 millions in 1954; £24,028 millions in 1959; £33,447 millions in 1964 and £45,133 millions in 1969.*

Include in the table, columns to show the percentage of total expenditure accounted for by the Public Sector at five-year intervals, and the percentage increase in public expenditure over each five-year interval.

B5   Dane Enterprises Ltd is a small manufacturing engineering company making plastic components for the aircraft industry. In 1969/70 it had a total sales income of £85,000 of which £26,000 was earned from its four largest customers. The corresponding figures for 1974/75 were £141,000 and £36,000, and for 1979/80 £242,000 and £52,000.

a. Construct pie charts to show the relative contribution to sales from the four largest customers in each of the three years.
b. Construct bar charts to show the same information.

B6   Two directors, from companies within the same group, are comparing their turnover figures, and are comparing the size of orders. They drew up the following table for 1,000 orders taken at random from their files:

	Company A	Company B
Orders*	Value(£)	Value(£)
1–100	1,239	226
101–200	1,652	340
201–300	2,065	452
301–400	2,478	538
401–500	3,304	708
501–600	3,717	1,415
601–700	4,543	1,981
701–800	4,956	4,245
801–900	6,195	5,943
901–1,000	11,151	12,452

* in increasing size.

Construct a Lorenz chart relating proportion of order value to proportion of total orders for each company.

B7   The following unemployment table appeared in a Central Office of Information leaflet in early 1977. Explain:

a. The unemployment position in the North-West over the period.
b. The relative levels of unemployment between the regions as shown in 1968 and 1975.

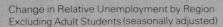

Change in Relative Unemployment by Region
Excluding Adult Students (seasonally adjusted)

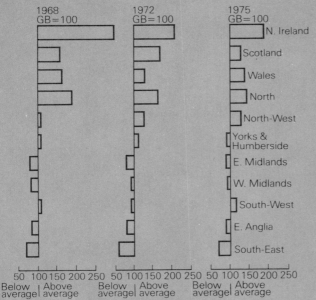

c. The level of unemployment in the North in 1975 if the seasonally adjusted national figure was 4½ per cent.

B8 The information given below is taken from the Report and Accounts of I.N.C. Ltd for the year 19x4.

a. Show that sales to the US have increased by 25 per cent between 19x0 and 19x4.

b. Find the comparable figure for the increase in sales to Europe.

c. If total sales continue to rise at approximately the same rate as between 19x1 and 19x4, the sales to the US increase by 20 per cent for each of the next two years, what angle of a pie chart for 19x6 would represent the US contribution to total sales?

d. If the total assets employed by the company were £250 m. in 19x0, and £300 m. in 19x4, construct a bar chart to compare profit as a percentage of total sales with profit as a percentage of total assets employed for 19x0 and 19x4.

Comment briefly on any tentative conclusions you might draw from this chart.

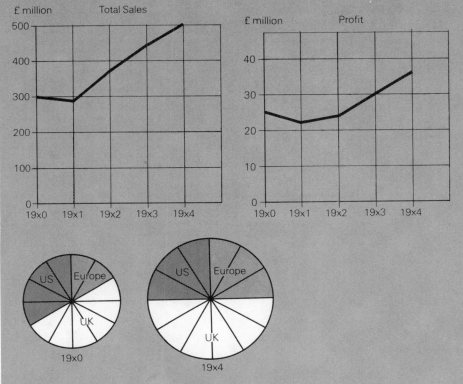

Analysis of Sales by Regions

Source: Cambridge Business Studies, A-level.

B9 The effectiveness and problems of the Social Contract may be shown
through four diagrams (opposite). Comment on the major features that
seem to arise from these. (The Social Contract was an 'understanding'
between the TUC and the Labour government. The TUC sought more
stable employment policies from government; the government sought
wage restraint.)

C. Essay Questions

C1 Explain how you would present a firm's accounts to:
a. The Board
b. The employees
c. The general public.

C2 Discuss why statisticians cannot confine their attentions to merely collecting and analysing data.

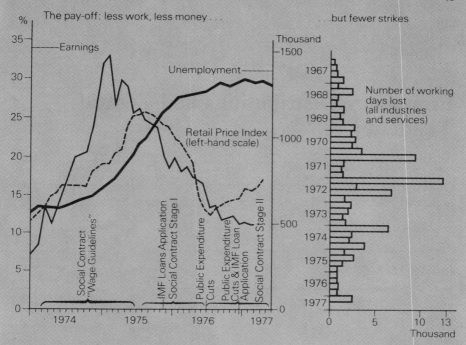

The pay-off: less work, less money . . . . . .but fewer strikes

%

Earnings

Unemployment

Retail Price Index
(left-hand scale)

Thousand
1500

1967

1968

1969

1970

1000

1971

1972

1973

500

1974

1975

1976

0

1977

Number of working
days lost
(all industries
and services)

Social Contract
"Wage Guidelines"

IMF Loans Application
Social Contract Stage I

Public Expenditure
Cuts

Public Expenditure
Cuts & IMF Loan
Application

Social Contract Stage II

1974   1975   1976   1977

0   5   10   13
Thousand

Squeezing the skilled

Hourly earnings for selected categories of engineering
workers as a % above those of labourers

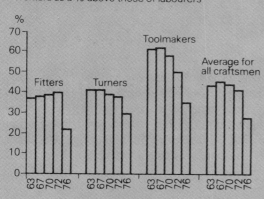

%

Fitters   Turners   Toolmakers   Average for
all craftsmen

63 67 70 72 76

The cost of the contract

As % of GDP at market prices

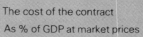
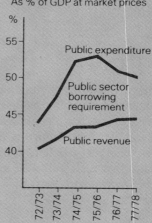

%

Public expenditure

Public sector
borrowing
requirement

Public revenue

72/73 73/74 74/75 75/76 76/77 77/78

Source: **The Economist**

Chapter 5

Frequency Distributions and Central Tendency

Objective: *To look at how large numbers of observations may be analysed in order to simplify interpretation by using various measures of central tendency.*

Plan of the chapter:

5.1 Case

Merrion has many buildings under its control, and in a typical year some 500,000 light bulbs are used in its premises. Whilst each is cheap, the high usage means that potential savings could be large. At present, the Council purchases its bulbs from the Sparklight Company but has received information that another supplier, Morelight Ltd is interested in tendering. Morelight claim that their bulbs are not only cheaper, but have a longer life. The Statistics Department is asked to give its views.

5.2 Introduction

The problem outlined above will be the theme for several chapters since it will require several statistical tools to provide an adequate answer. Whilst both manufacturers have claimed certain lifetimes, the scale of the buying means that Merrion should conduct its own study. The potential benefit runs into several thousands of pounds p.a., so the Council can afford to allocate staff time to the problem.

This is a fairly common problem in organisations, where large numbers of observations have to be handled, and where representative figures are required to give an overall summary picture. Examples include dimensional control in manufacturing, testing ammunition in the Services, or even university admissions through UCCA.

As a first step, information on the actual lives of Sparklight bulbs must be obtained. With the help of the electricians, a test rig was set up to measure bulb life. After a period of several months, the lives of 100 bulbs had been obtained. The results are shown in Fig. 5.1.

Lives of Sparklight Bulbs (to nearest hour)

688	705	696	691	729	685	719	728	716	700
691	707	679	690	720	691	722	712	715	706
692	735	712	706	717	695	681	694	729	708
702	696	713	698	741	674	697	693	710	668
727	710	749	698	650	699	747	691	692	706
722	708	700	673	682	696	689	736	690	694
698	676	666	698	658	702	685	683	689	688
665	683	661	733	685	683	707	718	671	701
701	695	692	677	708	721	681	664	697	693
718	717	684	703	709	704	726	725	699	713

Fig. 5.1: Raw data on bulb life

Clearly, in its present form, the data is of doubtful worth. It needs organising and analysing in order to show the underlying patterns.

5.3 Organising the Data

In order to reveal the patterns buried in the original data, one must restructure it.

5.3.1 Ordering the Data
The first step might be **ordering** the data into a sequence of ascending lives. Thus the lowest value (650 hr) is put first and the highest value (749 hr) last.

Some values will occur more than once (e.g. 666 hr). The ordered data is shown in Fig. 5.2.

Lives of Sparklight Bulbs (*to nearest hour*)

650	658	661	664	665	696	668	671	673	674
676	677	679	681	681	682	683	683	683	684
685	685	685	688	688	689	689	690	690	691
691	691	691	692	692	692	693	693	694	694
695	695	696	696	696	697	697	698	698	698
698	699	699	700	700	701	701	702	702	703
704	705	706	706	706	707	707	708	708	708
709	710	710	712	712	713	713	715	716	717
717	718	718	719	720	721	722	722	725	726
727	728	729	729	723	735	736	741	747	749

Fig. 5.2: Ordered bulb data

We now have a little more to go on, and can make a number of observations.
- The **range** of values is from 650 to 749, i.e. 99 hr.
- The most frequently occurring value, the **mode**, can be seen. Lives of 691 and 698 hr both occur four times.
- The value which splits the 100 observations into two equal halves, each of 50 values, the **median**, can be identified. (It is 698 hrs.)
- We could also calculate the **arithmetic mean** (or 'average') value by adding all values and dividing by the number of observations. (It is $\frac{69,987}{100} = 699.87$ hr.)

But useful as these observations are, we still cannot really see the underlying 'shape' of the data.

5.3.2 Grouped Data
Instead of recording individual bulb lives, we could divide the range into a number of groups. In general the number of groups (or **class intervals**) should be between eight and 15. (If fewer than eight are used, there may be a loss of arithmetic accuracy when using **grouped data** methods rather than the original data. If more than 15 are used, it becomes hard to assimilate the 'shape' of the data.)

Further, one should aim to ensure that no observation can fall on the boundary between two groups, and that the data within each group falls fairly evenly about the mid-point of that group (the **class mark**).

In the case of the Sparklight data, we could use ten groups, keeping a tally of the numbers within each to obtain the respective frequencies (Fig. 5.3).

Class (hr)	Tally	Frequency	Class mark (hr)
650–659	11	2	654.5
660–669	ʜʜ1	5	664.5
670–679	ʜʜ1 1	6	674.5
680–689	ʜʜ1 ʜʜ1 1111	14	684.5
690–699	ʜʜ1 ʜʜ1 ʜʜ1 ʜʜ1 ʜʜ1 1	26	694.5
700–709	ʜʜ1 ʜʜ1 ʜʜ1 111	18	704.5
710–719	ʜʜ1 ʜʜ1 111	13	714.5
720–729	ʜʜ1 ʜʜ1	10	724.5
730–739	111	3	734.5
740–749	111	3	744.5
		100	

Fig. 5.3: Grouped frequency data

The underlying pattern of the data is now more easily seen. It has a fairly symmetrical shape about a middle value. The histogram in Fig. 5.4 shows this clearly.

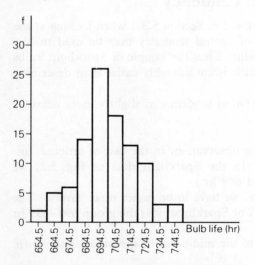

Fig. 5.4: Histogram of Sparklight bulb data

When presenting data in grouped frequency tables, use is sometimes made of open class intervals at each end of the table. This is done when a few of the observations fall quite far away from the range of other observations. For example, if we took a sample of 100 men and measured their heights we might find that perhaps 97 men fell within the height range of 1.50 m and 2.10 m but that the three others were 1.25 m, 1.37 m and 2.30 m. Rather than have lots of empty class intervals, the group frequency table might be presented in the following way:

$$< 1.50$$
$$1.50 < 1.52$$
$$1.52 < 1.54$$
$$.$$
$$.$$
$$.$$
$$2.08 < 2.10$$
$$> 2.10$$

with <1.50 and >2.10 being the open class intervals.

Only a small number of observations will be found in these open-ended class intervals. The statistician may, if desired, carry out any calculations using the values given by the raw data, rather than assume that some 'mid-point' accurately reflects the arithmetic average of the interval as we would do in other, non-open-ended classes. Thus for the class <1.50, it would be appropriate to use the two observations 1.25 and 1.37. Similarly for the class >2.10 it would also be appropriate to use the actual observation 2.30.

5.4 Measures of Central Tendency

We have briefly mentioned three of these in Section 5.3.1 when looking at the ordered Sparklight data. Measures of central tendency may be used to 'describe' the distribution in a single value. Thus the sample of Sparklight bulbs has an average life of 699.87 hr (which is considerably easier than describing the whole distribution!).

Let us now look at measures of central tendency in slightly more detail.

5.4.1 The Mode
This is the most frequently occurring observation. In the case of ordered, ungrouped data, it is easy to spot. (In the Sparklight data of Fig. 5.2, we observed two modal values, 691 and 698 hr.)

When working with grouped data, we have to be rather more careful. The *modal interval* is fairly easy to find. (For Sparklight, it is the group 690–699 hr containing 26 observations.)

The *crude mode* is then taken as to the mid-point of the modal interval (in the Sparklight case, 694.5 hr).

However, the *interpolated mode* gives a more accurate figure than the crude mode, and is calculated from:

$$\text{Interpolated Mode} = L + \left\{ \frac{fa}{(fa+fb)} \times C \right\}$$

Where L = Lower limit of modal interval
fa = Frequency of interval *following* the modal group
fb = Frequency of interval *preceding* the modal group
C = The class interval.

For the Sparklight data:
L = 690 (lowest limit of interval 690–699)
fa =   18 (for the interval 700–709)
fb =   14 (for the interval 680–689)
C =   10 (the width of the interval)

and so the Interpolated Mode $= 690 + \left\{ \dfrac{18}{18+14} \times 10 \right\}$
$$= 690 + 5.63$$
$$= \underline{695.63 \text{ hr}}$$

5.4.2 The Median
This is the value which divides the data into two equal halves. We saw that 698 hr was the median of the Sparklight data.

Where the number of observations is *odd*, there will be a single median observation. Thus in a sample of 101 observations, it will be the 51st from either end. Where the number of observations is *even*, the median is found by taking the average (arithmetic mean) of the *two* middle observations. So in the Sparklight case it was $\dfrac{698 + 698}{2}$ = 698 hr, since both the 50th and 51st observation were 698 hr.

5.4.3 The Arithmetic Mean
When asked to calculate a measure of central tendency, most people would work out the arithmetic mean (probably using the common, but less precise, name of 'the average'). The arithmetic mean is only one mean, others being the **geometric mean** and the harmonic mean. But it *is* the most commonly used and understood mean.

The Arithmetic mean is calculated from *ungrouped data* by adding together all the observations and dividing by the number of observations. When working with *grouped data*, the essential method is unchanged. As before, we are interested in two things, the total number of observations and the sum of all the observations.

The first poses no problems; it is the sum of all the frequencies for each class interval. (In shorthand Σf). The second is more difficult because individual observations have lost their individual values. Hence we must take the mid-point of each class interval (the class mark) as being representative of the values within it. The total value of each class interval is therefore:

Frequency × mid-point of class interval (or in shorthand Σfx).

★   The arithmetic mean ($\bar{x}$) is therefore:

$$\bar{x} = \frac{\Sigma fx}{\Sigma f}$$

Using the Sparklight data, we can calculate the arithmetic mean, as shown in Fig. 5.5.

Class interval	Class mark (x)	Frequency (f)	Class mark × frequency (fx)
650–659	654.5	2	1,309
660–669	664.5	5	3,322.5
670–679	674.5	6	4,047
680–689	684.5	14	9,583
690–699	694.5	26	18,057
700–709	704.5	18	12,681
710–719	714.5	13	9,288.5
720–729	724.5	10	7,245
730–739	734.5	3	2,203.5
740–749	744.5	3	2,233.5
		$\Sigma f = 100$	$\Sigma fx = 69,970$

Fig. 5.5: Calculation of arithmetic mean from grouped data

So $\bar{x} = \dfrac{\Sigma fx}{\Sigma f} = \underline{699.70}.$

Compare this with the true mean of 699.87 and the error caused by grouping the data can be seen to be small. A larger sample would have reduced the error still further.

This process is rather tedious, and we can reduce the slog by *assuming* a mean from the outset and then calculating the **deviation** of the class interval mid-points from it. To reduce the calculation needed, it is best to select one of the class interval mid-points as an *assumed mean*. Let us take 694.5 as an assumed mean, and calculate the deviations and total deviations shown in Fig. 5.6.

★ **See Questions B1 to B3**

Class interval	Mid-point of class (x)	Frequency (f)	Deviation (d)	Total deviation = frequency × deviation
650–659	654.5	2	−40	−80
660–669	664.5	5	−30	−150
670–679	674.5	6	−20	−120
680–689	684.5	14	−10	−140
690–699	694.5 (Assumed mean)	26	0	0
700–709	704.5	18	+10	+180
710–719	714.5	13	+20	+260
720–729	724.5	10	+30	+300
730–739	734.5	3	+40	+120
740–749	744.5	3	+50	+150
		$\Sigma f = 100$		$\Sigma fd = +520$

Fig. 5.6: Calculation of arithmetic mean from an assumed mean

Since Σfd is positive, we have *under*-estimated the value of the true mean, so we must *add* the average deviation to our assumed value.

$$\text{Arithmetic mean} = \text{Assumed mean} + \left\{ \frac{\Sigma fd}{\Sigma f} \right\}$$
$$= 694.5 + \frac{520}{100}$$
$$= 694.5 + 5.20$$
$$= \underline{699.70 \text{ hr.}}$$

5.4.4. The Geometric Mean

The arithmetic mean is not the only one that can be calculated and one other which is sometimes used is the geometric mean. Its value is that it is based upon the product of the numbers rather than their sum and hence the effect of extreme values is reduced. It is not in common use, partly because the great majority of business problems behave in a reasonably symmetrical way and the arithmetic mean is good enough and much easier to calculate.

The geometric mean is calculated by multiplying the observations together, and then finding the *n*th root of the result (where *n* is the number of observations).

As a simple example, suppose we have four observations, 2, 3, 4, 12.

$$\text{Arithmetic mean} = \frac{2 + 3 + 4 + 12}{4} = \underline{5.25}$$

$$\text{Geometric mean} = \sqrt[4]{2 \times 3 \times 4 \times 12} = \sqrt[4]{288} = \underline{4.12}$$

As you can see the geometric mean is much less affected by the large observation than is the arithmetic mean. This valuable feature is used in the calculation of the Financial Times Index because there may, at any one time, be one or two shares which move dramatically. The F.T. Index uses the geometric mean of the values of 30 selected shares.

5.5 Comparing the Measures of Centrality

Let us concentrate on the three commonly used measures, the arithmetic mean, the median and the mode. For the Sparklight data, the values were:

Arithmetic mean = 699.70 hr
Median   = 698   hr
Mode   = 695.63 hr

The three values are in fairly close agreement, and hence the decision which measure to use is not greatly significant. On balance, the arithmetic mean is the most likely, since it can be used in subsequent analyses.
Consider however the three distributions below:

Distribution A   8 10 12 12 13 14 15
Distribution B   1   2   2   4   6   9 60
Distribution C   1 13 13 13 14 14 16

Distribution	Arith. mean	Median	Mode
A	12	12	12
B	12	4	2
C	12	13	13

In distribution B and C, the results are distorted by outlying values (60 in B and 1 in C). It is clear that in such cases the median is less affected than the other two measures.

It is also clear that frequency distributions cannot be defined solely in terms of measures of central tendency, but that some consideration must also be made for the *spread* of the data. Chapter 6 deals with this aspect of statistical enquiry.

★ See Question B4
★★ See Question B5

Work Section

A. Revision Questions

A1 What is meant by 'ordering' data?

A2 What factors should be borne in mind when grouping data?

A3 Define class interval and class mark.

A4 Distinguish between the median and the mode.

A5 Distinguish between a crude mode and an interpolated mode for grouped data.

A6 How would you determine the median from an even number of observations.

A7 What basic assumption is made in determining a. the arithmetic mean and b. the median from grouped data.

A8 What is an 'assumed mean' and what is the advantage of the assumption?

A9 When might it be preferable to use the geometric mean rather than the arithmetic mean?

A10 Which of the measures arithmetic mean, median, mode are
   a. most affected by outlying values?
   b. least affected by outlying values?
   c. unaffected by outlying values?

B. Exercises/Case Studies

B1 The weekly output of components from a small factory was recorded over a period of 50 weeks. The results were:

Output:	10	110	112	113	114	115	116	117	118
No./weeks:	1	2	5	7	8	10	9	6	2

   a. Determine the mean, median and mode values.
   b. Discuss which is the most appropriate measure.

B2 The following table shows the earnings of semi-skilled production workers at the 'Morelight' lamp factory.

Hourly earnings (£)	Employees
2.20–2.29	12
2.30–2.39	14
2.40–2.49	18
2.50–2.59	20
2.60–2.69	48
2.70–2.79	34
2.80–2.89	17
2.90–2.99	15
3.00–3.09	10
3.10–3.19	9
3.20–3.29	3

    a. Why do you think that the earnings show such a wide variation?

    b. Determine the arithmetic mean wage by *two* different methods.

    c. Determine the modal wage.

B3 The output of a spindle grinding machine was measured and the results appear below:

Diameter of spindle (cm)	Number of spindles
0.940–0.949	1
0.950–0.959	6
0.960–0.969	64
0.970–0.979	215
0.980–0.989	401
0.990–0.999	616
1.000–1.009	411
1.010–1.019	227
1.020–1.029	49
1.030–1.039	9
1.040–1.049	1

    a. What is the size of class interval used?

    b. What are the class marks of the respective intervals?

    c. What is the modal interval?

    d. What is the arithmetic mean spindle diameter?

B4 A firm which services washing machines is trying to determine where to locate a new headquarters for its fleet of service vans. The area to be served consists of nine towns lying on a motorway.

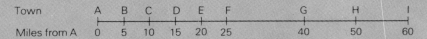

Town	A	B	C	D	E	F	G	H	I
Miles from A	0	5	10	15	20	25	40	50	60

The manager decides to use the mean of the distances from A to determine his choice of location. His assistant suggests that the median would be a better measure to use.
a. Which town does each man nominate?
b. Calculate the mean distance of the nine towns from both of those suggested as a possible headquarters.
c. The number of service calls to each town in the last month were:

Town A B C D E F G H I
Calls 7 13 6 8 12 3 4 7 5

State where, on all the information now presented, the headquarters should be sited and justify your choice.
d. What other factors not mentioned might affect the decision?

(Cambridge Local Syndicate A Level)

B5 Candidates in an examination had the following marks on each of two papers:

	Marks	0–9	10–19	20–29	30–39	40–49
No. of	Paper 1:	1	4	7	11	16
Students	Paper 2:	0	1	8	12	24

	Marks	50–59	60–69	70–79	80–89
No. of	Paper 1:	13	11	6	1
Students	Paper 2:	20	3	2	0

Comment on these results.

B6 The following data relates to statistics on labour disputes.

No. of man-days lost	No. of disputes
Below 250	1,200
251–500	453
501–1,000	402
1,001–5,000	592
5,001–25,000	180
25,001–50,000	23

a. Plot the results on a frequency distribution diagram.
b. Which measure of centrality would you use, and why?

C. Essay Questions

C1 Explain why the 'average' (arithmetic mean) is not necessarily the best method of central tendency. Give examples to support your arguments.

C2 Advise each of the following which measure of centrality they should use, supporting your advice with reasoned argument and illustration where appropriate:

a. The buyer for the shoe department of a store.
b. The compiler of an index, inputs to which are expected to vary considerably.
c. The research scientist analysing experimental data.
d. An inspector reporting on the number of passengers carried and the frequency with which bus stops on the route are used.

Chapter 6

Measures of Spread

Objective: *To consider methods of defining the 'spread' of data from observations.*

Plan of the chapter:

6.1 Introduction

In the previous chapter, we saw how the mean, median and mode could be used to define the centre of distribution. But the central measure alone cannot wholly describe the distribution, as Fig. 6.1 shows.

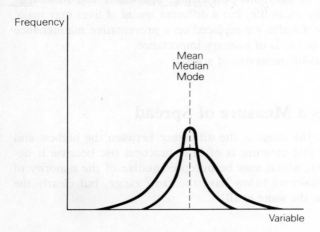

Fig. 6.1: Two distributions with same central measures

Both distributions are symmetrical (shown by having coincident mean, median and mode) and both have the same value for all three measures. Yet clearly one distribution is far tighter than the other.

Other distributions may not be symmetrical, and it may be harder to assess the underlying pattern of spread. The two distributions in Fig. 6.2 illustrate this.

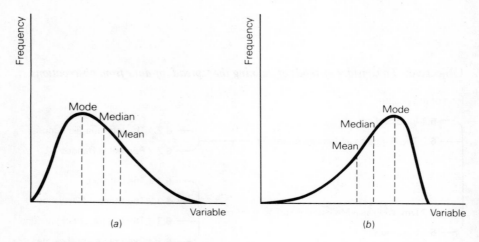

Fig. 6.2: Asymmetric distributions

Figure 6.2 (*a*) show a distribution where the tail is longer to the right (called a *positive* skew) whilst in (*b*) the tail is to the left (a *negative* skew). Note how the mean, median and mode no longer coincide as they did for a symmetrical distribution.

In Merrion's problem of lightbulb purchasing, Sparklight and Morelight bulbs might have the same mean life, but a different *spread* of lives may make one preferable, especially if bulbs are replaced on a preventative maintenance basis, where consistency of life is of primary importance.

Let us now look at possible measures of spread.

6.2 The Range as a Measure of Spread

As we saw in Chapter 5, the range is the difference between the highest and lowest observed values. The measure is of little practical use because it depends on only two values, which may be unrepresentative of the majority of our data. The two distributions below have the same range, but clearly the 'spread' of the data is not the same at all!

Distribution A	1	2	3	4	5	6	7	8	9	10	11
Distribution B	1	6	6	6	6	6	6	6	6	6	11

We need a method of definition which will take into account the middle portion of the distribution as well as the extremes.

6.2.1 The Interquartile Range

You will recall that the median was the value which split the data into two equal halves. Half of the observations lay on each side of the median value. Why not split the data into *four* equal parts? The values which lie at the boundaries of each quarter are called **quartiles**.

Lets look back at the ordered Sparklight data:

Sparklight Bulb Lives (to nearest hour)

650	658	661	664	665	666	668	671	673	674
676	677	679	681	681	682	683	683	683	684
685	685	685	688	688	689	689	690	690	691
691	691	691	692	692	692	693	693	694	694
695	695	696	696	696	697	697	698	698	698
698	699	699	700	700	701	701	702	702	703
704	705	706	706	706	707	707	708	708	708
709	710	710	712	712	713	713	715	716	717
717	718	718	719	720	721	722	722	725	726
727	728	729	729	733	735	736	741	747	749

Fig. 6.3: Ordered bulb life data

Since there are 100 observations, the quartiles will separate the data into four 'packets' of 25 observations.

The **lower quartile** (Q_1) is 688.5.
The **intermediate quartile** (Q_2) is 698 (i.e. the median).
The **upper quartile** (Q_3) is 712.5.
If grouped data is being used, the general process is the same.

Class interval	Class mark (x)	Frequency (f)	Cumulative frequency
650–659	654.5	2	2
660–669	664.5	5	7
670–679	674.5	6	13
680–689	684.5	14	27
690–699	694.5	26	53
700–709	704.5	18	71
710–719	714.5	13	84
720–729	724.5	10	94
730–739	734.5	3	97
740–749	744.5	3	100

Fig. 6.4: Sparklight bulb lives; grouped data

We know that the 25th observation (Q_1) lies in the range 680–689, the 50th (Q_2) in the range 690–699 and the 75th (Q_3) in the range 710–719. To find out exactly where Q_1 occurs, we assume that the 14 values in the class interval 680–689 are evenly distributed. We also know that 13 bulbs have lives of 679 hr or less. So the 25th lies 12 bulbs into the range, and the value can be interpolated using:

$679 + \left(\dfrac{12}{14} \times 10\right)$ hr $= 679 + 8.6$ hr $= \underline{687.6 \text{ hr.}}$ (The interquartile range for ungrouped data is $712.5 - 688.5 = 24.0$ hr.)

For the third quartile: $709 + \left(\dfrac{4}{13} \times 10\right)$ hr $= 709 + 3.08$ hr $= \underline{712.08 \text{ hr.}}$

The **interquartile range** is the distance between the first and third quartiles, and so from the grouped data:

$712.08 - 687.60 = \underline{24.48 \text{ hr.}}$

Thus we can see that 50 per cent of the bulbs will have lives of between 687.60 and 712.08 hr. (688.5 and 712.5 hr for ungrouped data.)

6.2.2 Percentile Ranges

For certain types of study with large samples, dividing the range using quartiles may be too coarse. For this reason, the observations may be divided into one hundred equal parts rather than four, the dividing lines between successive hundredths being percentiles. This approach is often encountered in psychological testing, where an individual's score on a test is related to the population percentiles.

Quartiles and percentiles make use of more information than the range, but do not lend themselves to further statistical treatment. For this reason, they are less common than measures of spread based on the deviations of data.

6.3 Deviation as a Measure of Spread

The deviation of value (d) is the difference between the arithmetic mean ($\bar{x}$) and the value in question (x):

$$d = (x - \bar{x})$$

Can this be used as a measure of spread?
Consider a simple distribution of I.Q. scores: 110, 112, 113, 117, 123.
The arithmetic mean ($\bar{x}$) is (110 + 112 + 113 + 117 + 123) ÷ 5 = 115.
We could work out the deviations of each value from the mean:

x	$d \ (= x - \bar{x})$
110	−5
112	−3
113	−2
117	+2
123	+8
	0

The *total* deviation is zero, which should not surprise us if we recall the method of calculating arithmetic means using an assumed mean.
We *could* ignore the signs of deviation, and so obtain a mean **deviation** of (5+3+2+2+8) ÷ 5 = 4. But ignoring signs is not very mathematical!

6.3.1 The Variance

The mathematical way of removing signs is to square the quantity. We could then calculate a mean squared deviation (known as the **variance**). Suppose a frequency distribution of test marks produced the following result:

Marks:	15	17	19	23	26	30
Frequency:	1	1	3	9	4	2

The arithmetic mean is found from:

$$\bar{x} = \frac{\Sigma fx}{\Sigma f} = \frac{460}{20} = 23.0.$$

The variance is found as follows:

Marks (x)	Frequency (f)	Deviation $d\ (=(x - \bar{x}))$	Squared deviation $(d)^2$	$f.(d)^2$
15	1	-8	64	64
17	1	-6	36	36
19	3	-4	16	48
23	9	0	0	0
26	4	$+3$	9	36
30	2	$+7$	49	98
	$\Sigma f = 20$			$\Sigma fd^2 = 282$

Hence **variance** $= \dfrac{\Sigma fd^2}{\Sigma f} = \dfrac{282}{20} = \underline{14.1}.$

Fig. 6.5: Calculating the variance

Had the original data been grouped, we would have used the mid-points of each class interval to represent the x values.

But a slight problem with the variance lies in the units. As it stands, the variance calculated above is in the units of marks², whereas the mean etc. are based on the unit of marks.

6.3.2 The Standard Deviation

If we take the positive square root of the variance, we can return to our original units. The quantity, the square root of the mean squared deviation, is known by the more manageable name of standard deviation.

Whilst most calculators have a key for calculating the standard deviation directly, the engineer's name for it – root mean squared deviation – is a useful way of remembering what it involves should the battery go flat on a Sunday afternoon! (Take the square *root* of the *mean* of the *squared deviation*). As a formula, it looks like:

$$SD\ (\sigma) = \sqrt{\frac{\Sigma f(x-\bar{x})^2}{\Sigma f}} \quad \text{or} \quad \sqrt{\frac{\Sigma fd^2}{\Sigma f}}$$

For the Sparklight data, the process would be as shown below. (The arithmetic mean life ($\bar{x}$) was 699.7 hr.)

Class interval	Class mark (x)	Frequency (f)	Deviation $d(=(x-\bar{x}))$	d^2	$f.d^2$
650–659	654.5	2	−45.2	2,043	4,086
660–669	664.5	5	−35.2	1,239	6,195
670–679	674.5	6	−25.2	635	3,810
680–689	684.5	14	−15.2	231	3,234
690–699	694.5	26	− 5.2	27	703
700–709	704.5	18	+ 4.8	23	414
710–719	714.5	13	+14.8	219	2,847
720–729	724.5	10	+24.8	615	6,150
730–739	734.5	3	+34.8	1,211	3,633
740–749	744.5	3	+44.8	2,007	6,021
		$\Sigma f = 100$			$\Sigma f.d^2 = 37,093$

$$SD = \sqrt{\frac{\Sigma f.d^2}{\Sigma f}} = \sqrt{\frac{37,093}{100}} = \sqrt{370.93} = \underline{19.3 \text{ hr.}}$$

Fig. 6.6: Calculating the standard deviation for Sparklight bulbs

The above method is time consuming, but luckily there is a short cut when using grouped data using an assumed mean. This is useful when calculating both mean and standard deviation at the same time. The method is shown in Fig. 6.7 below:

Class mark (x)	Frequency (f)	Deviation from assumed mean (d)	d^2	f.d	$f.d^2$
654.5	2	−40	1,600	− 80	3,200
664.5	5	−30	900	−150	4,500
674.5	6	−20	400	−120	2,400
684.5	14	−10	100	−140	1,400
694.5	26	0	0	0	0
704.5	18	+10	100	+180	1,800
714.5	13	+20	400	+260	5,200
724.5	10	+30	900	+300	9,000
734.5	3	+40	1,600	+120	4,800
744.5	3	+50	2,500	+150	7,500
	$\Sigma f = 100$			$\Sigma fd = +520$	$\Sigma f(d)^2 = 39,800$

ssumed ean

Fig. 6.7: A short-cut calculation of standard deviation

And the quick method: $SD = \sqrt{\dfrac{\Sigma f(d)^2}{\Sigma f} - \left(\dfrac{\Sigma f.d}{\Sigma f}\right)^2}$

$$= \sqrt{\dfrac{39,800}{100} - \left(\dfrac{520}{100}\right)^2}$$

$$= \sqrt{398 - 27.04}$$

$$= \sqrt{371}$$

$$= \underline{19.3 \text{ hr}} \text{ which is the same result as before.}$$

This method is probably quicker than pushing buttons on a calculator!

Let us summarise the main methods used to determine the spread of the Sparklight data in the frequency polygon of Fig. 6.8:

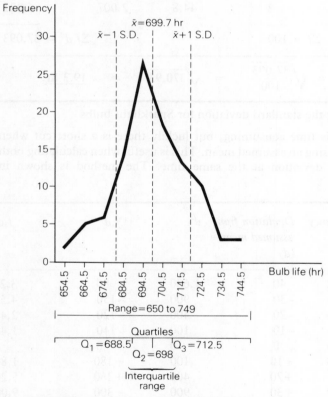

Fig. 6.8: Measures of spread for Sparklight data

6.3.3 The Coefficient of Variation

With the exception of the variance, all of the measures of spread considered are measured in the same units as the original data. When looking at data measured in *different* units, comparison is difficult. Chapter 9 will look at one way round this, but a simple measure is the **coefficient of variation**, calculated by:

$$\text{Coefficient of variation} = \frac{\text{Standard deviation}}{\text{Arithmetic mean}} \times 100\%$$

In the case of Sparklight, this becomes:

$$\frac{19.3}{699.7} \times 100\% = \underline{2.76\%}$$

Note how the coefficient is now a dimensionless number, whatever the original units.

6.3.4 Skewness Coefficients
We began the chapter with a qualitative look at skewed distributions. Let us end by expressing skewness in quantitative terms. A measure of the skewness of a distribution is provided by the **skewness coefficient**.

$$\text{Skewness coefficient} = \frac{\text{Mean} - \text{Mode}}{\text{Standard deviation}}$$

For positive skew, the coefficient will be positive, whilst negative skews give a negative coefficient. The larger the coefficient, the greater the skewness of the data.

6.4 Summary

Let us briefly summarise the various measures of spread and their usefulness to us:

The Range: Relies on only two values, and hence easily affected by extreme values.

The Interquartile Range: Relatively quick to measure but does not allow for further statistical interpretation.

Percentiles: Often used to show the inequality of distributions (especially in economics) but again capable of limited statistical interpretation.

Mean Deviation: Automatically equals zero unless we decide to ignore the signs of deviations. Quick to calculate, but not capable of further manipulation.

Variance: A valuable statistical tool (although not used further in this text) capable of being used in complex analyses. Suffers from problem of units being squared.

Standard Deviation: The most valuable and widely used measure of spread, which will be met again in Chapters 9 and 10. Has a positive value even with symmetrical distributions.

Work Section

A. Revision Questions

A1 Define the range of a distribution. Why is it an unsuitable measure of spread?

A2 What is the interquartile deviation?

A3 Distinguish between positive and negative skew in a distribution.

A4 How are the median and intermediate quartile related?

A5 What is the value of total deviation for any distribution?

A6 How does the variance overcome the problems associated with the mean deviation?

A7 How are the variance and standard deviation related?

A8 Give a formula for calculating the standard deviation.

A9 For what is root mean squared deviation another name?

A10 Which of the measures of spread can be used in further statistical analysis?

B. Exercises/Case Studies

B1 Sales per day were recorded for a shop with the following results:

Sales/day (£)	600–649	650–699	700–749	750–799	800–849	850–899	900–949
Frequency:	2	4	8	15	10	7	4

Calculate a. The mean daily sales.
b. The interquartile deviation.
c. The variance.
d. The standard deviation.

B2 Measure the heights or weights of a large (50+) sample of your fellow students. Analyse and comment on your results.

B3 The following marks were obtained in an examination. You are asked to examine them and comment on the results obtained.

30	32	36	32	36	35	52	33	31	40
32	35	31	75	34	39	37	55	39	78
40	46	45	35	37	38	33	56	36	48
35	2	36	52	38	41	53	38	35	39
45	30	36	41	43	31	37	62	32	48
39	38	35	39	47	37	59	35	39	42

    a. Order and group the data.

    b. Determine the interquartile range.

    c. Determine the mean and standard deviation.

    d. Plot your results and comment on the candidates' performance.

B4 If you have access to a computer, write programs which will

    a. sort raw data into order;

    b. produce a grouped frequency distribution;

    c. produce a histogram of the grouped data;

    d. print the mean, median and standard deviation.

B5 If you have a calculator, look up how to enter and calculate statistical quantities such as the arithmetic mean, variance and standard deviation. Use a calculator to evaluate answers to B3(c). (With some calculators, data can be entered directly.)

B6 Calculate the variance and standard deviation for each of the following sets of numbers:

    6 9 3 2 7 8
   16 19 13 12 17 18
   96 99 93 92 97 98

    Comment on your results.

B7 For the following data on employment:

Age (Yr)	Numbers employed (m.)
15 to <20	1.1
20 to <25	1.7
25 to <30	1.5
30 to <35	1.3
35 to <40	1.3
40 to <45	1.4
45 to <50	1.5
50 to <55	1.3
55 to <60	1.4
60 to <65	1.1
65 to <70	0.4

    a. Plot the data as a frequency polygon and cumulative percentage graph.

    b. Calculate the standard deviation.

    c. Calculate the interquartile range.

C. Essay Questions

C1 Discuss the methods of measuring spread of data likely to be of most use to:

    a. An economist studying income distribution.

    b. A psychologist conducting vocational guidance tests.

    c. A market researcher looking at differences in sales patterns between the north and south of the country.

    d. A quality control manager interested in the consistency of production.

C2 Of what is standard deviation a measure? Give *three* examples (in contexts as different as possible) where it would be useful to know the standard deviation of a set of observations.

(Cambridge Local Examinations Syndicate A Level)

Part II   Uncertainty in Decisions
Chapter 7

Probability and Decision Trees

Objectives: *To show how uncertainty can be quantified by the use of probability, and how the economic consequences and risks of decision making can be combined using decision trees.*

Plan of the chapter:

- 7.1 Case
- 7.2 Rules of Probability
  - 7.2.1 The Rule of Proportions
  - 7.2.2 A Probability Scale
  - 7.2.3 The Addition Rule
  - 7.2.4 The Multiplication Rule
  - 7.2.5 Probability Tree Diagrams
- 7.3 Decision Trees

7.1 Case

Merrion's Estates department has a vacant plot of industrial land which it wishes to dispose of. Three possibilities exist: the Council could sell the land to a developer, it could develop the infrastructure only (roads and sewage) and then sell to a developer, or it could decide to develop the whole site itself and sell the factories. Any development of the site would carry both costs and risks; developers might not wish to take on a part-finished site or buyers might not be found should Merrion build factories. Much depends on the economic outlook for the next year, and it may be better to wait to sell the site then (but if this happens, finance would *not* be available to do any development work on the site).

This case contains an element that is all too familiar to any organisation. There is uncertainty about the outcomes of decisions. Yet we are used to the quantification of *uncertainty* in everyday life. If told, 'There is an 80 per cent chance of rain tomorrow' we would probably have second thoughts about taking a picnic lunch to the coast. Similarly, a visit to a racecourse should provide other examples! When quantifying in such cases we are not removing the uncertainty, for that is clearly impossible. The mathematical treatment of uncertain outcomes is based on **probability**.

7.2 **Rules of Probability**

There are a number of relatively simple rules which will help in the quantification of uncertain situations.

7.2.1 **The Rule of Proportions**

This offers a way of giving a value to the probability of an outcome. The rule states that where there is more than one possible outcome in a given situation, the probability of any one of them occurring will be given by:

Total no. of ways in which the desired result can occur
Total no. of ways in which all possible outcomes can occur

> *Example: Suppose that a box containing 100 brass washers was inadvertently tipped into a bin containing 900 similarly sized steel washers, and subsequently thoroughly mixed with them. If one washer is removed, what is the probability that it will be a brass one?*
>
> *Since there are 100 possible ways of selecting a brass washer and 1,000 washers that could be chosen, the probability ($P_{(brass)}$ in shorthand) is:*

$$P_{(brass)} = \frac{100}{1,000} = 0.1 \ (or \ 10\%)$$

In subsequent sections, it will be important to remember that *all* possible outcomes must be considered.

7.2.2 **A Probability Scale**

It is conventional to give absolute certainty a value of 1 and absolute impossibility a value of 0. Intermediate values will therefore imply uncertainty of outcome. A few examples are shown in Fig. 7.1 below:

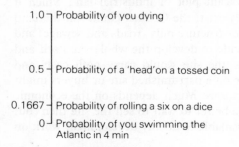

1.0 — Probability of you dying

0.5 — Probability of a 'head' on a tossed coin

0.1667 — Probability of rolling a six on a dice

0 — Probability of you swimming the Atlantic in 4 min

Fig. 7.1: A probability scale

This 'rule' is rather valuable, since it can reduce the amount of calculation needed in later sections. This is because the total probability of all possible outcomes in a given case *must* be 1.

7.2.3 The Addition Rule

This states that:

Where several possible, and mutually exclusive, outcomes can occur, the probability of alternative results occurring is found by adding the probabilities of the individual events.

> *Example: What is the probability that a die will show* either *a 5* or *6 in a single throw? Here, the outcomes* are *mutually exclusive (a 5 precludes the result being a 6!). The probability of a 5 is 1/6, as is the probability of a 6. So the required result*
>
> $$P_{(5\ or\ 6)} = P_{(5)} + P_{(6)} = \tfrac{1}{6} + \tfrac{1}{6} = \underline{\underline{\tfrac{1}{3}}}$$
>
> *(This could also be derived from the formula in Section 7.2.1 since there are two desired outcomes out of six possible.)*

Combining this rule with the information in Section 7.2.2, we can save time in some cases:

> *Example: What is the probability of getting less than 5 in a throw of a single die? We* could *calculate this from:*
>
> $$P_{(less\ than\ 5)} = P_{(1)} + P_{(2)} + P_{(3)} + P_{(4)}$$
>
> *but it would be quicker to say*
>
> $$\begin{aligned} P_{(less\ than\ 5)} &= 1 - (P_{(5\ or\ 6)}) \\ &= 1 - (P_5 + P_6) \\ &= 1 - \tfrac{1}{3} = \underline{\underline{\tfrac{2}{3}.}} \end{aligned}$$

7.2.4 The Multiplication Rule

This states that when several mutually exclusive results can occur, the probability of getting a particular combination of results will be obtained by multiplying the probability of individual outcomes.

> Example: *What is the probability of getting two sixes from two dice? In this case:*
>
> $$\begin{aligned} P_{(6\ then\ 6)} &= P_{(6)} \times P_{(6)} \\ &= \tfrac{1}{6} \times \tfrac{1}{6} = \underline{\underline{\tfrac{1}{36}}} \end{aligned}$$ ★
>
> *since the outcome of the second die is not affected by that of the first.*

Let us consider an example which will illustrate these 'rules'.

★ See Questions B1 to B7

Example: Two firms each maintain their own lorries. To cut costs, they are considering setting up a joint repair depot. Both fleets were studied for 100 days, and showed the following pattern of breakdowns.

No. of lorries off the road	0	1	2	3
No. of days (Firm A)	20	30	40	10
No. of days (Firm B)	30	10	40	20

The manager wants to know how many lorries a combined depot might expect. Using the approach of Section 7.2.1, we can see that the probability of getting a particular number of breakdowns in each fleet will be:

Probability of obtaining

	0	1	2	3
Firm A	0.2	0.3	0.4	0.1
Firm B	0.3	0.1	0.4	0.2

On a particular day, Firm A might have 0, 1, 2 or 3 breakdowns whilst (independently) Firm B might also have 0, 1, 2 or 3 breakdowns.

There are then 16 ways in which a combined depot might receive lorries. The probability of any particular mix occurring may be found by using the 'multiplication rule' of Section 7.2.4.

No. from Firm A	and	No. from Firm B
0		0
0		1
0		2
0		3
1		0
1		1
1		2
1		3
2		0
2		1
2		2
2		3
3		0
3		1
3		2
3		3

The probability of the combined depot getting, say, three lorries on a particular day is obtained from using the addition and multiplication rules of Sections 7.2.3 and 7.2.4.

		Probability
EITHER:	*0 from A* AND *3 from B*	$(0.2) \times (0.2) = 0.04$
		$+$
OR:	*1 from A* AND *2 from B*	$(0.3) \times (0.4) = 0.12$
		$+$
OR:	*2 from A* AND *1 from B*	$(0.4) \times (0.1) = 0.04$
		$+$
OR:	*3 from A* AND *0 from B*	$(0.1) \times (0.3) = 0.03$
		————
		0.23

Hence we would expect a total 3 lorries to break down with a probability of 0.23. Repeating the process for 0, 1, 2 . . . . . 6 lorries in the combined depot gives the following probabilities. (You might check this for yourself.)

No. of Lorries off road	*Probability*
0	*0.06*
1	*0.11*
2	*0.23*
3	*0.23*
4	*0.23*
5	*0.12*
6	*0.02*
	————
	1.00
	————

So if the firms provide repair bays for only four lorries in the depot, they will have lorries waiting, on average, on 14 per cent of occasions. What number of bays to plan for depends on the relative costs of repair facilities being idle and lorries being off the road. What is the average number of lorries off the road on a given day? To find this, we multiply the outcome by its probability to find the **expected value.**

No. of lorries off road	$\times$ *Probability*	$=$ *Expected value*
0	*0.06*	*0*
1	*0.11*	*0.11*
2	*0.23*	*0.46*
3	*0.23*	*0.69*
4	*0.23*	*0.92*
5	*0.12*	*0.60*
6	*0.02*	*0.12*
		————
		2.90
		————

Over a given period, one would therefore expect an average of 2.90 lorries per day to be off the road. Note that the probabilities are showing what one would expect to occur on average, over a large number of days. Probability says nothing about what one might expect to happen on a *particular* day.

7.2.5 Probability Tree Diagrams

In cases such as that of the combined repair depot just considered, it is all too easy to overlook one or more possible outcomes. A tool which might help us to overcome this is the **probability tree**. As the name suggests, this is a branching diagram which shows all the possible outcomes in a given case. Figure 7.2 below shows such a tree diagram for the lorries example.

Breakdowns from Firm A (and probability)	Breakdowns from Firm B (and probability)	Combined total of breakdowns	Probability $(P_A \times P_B)$
0 (0.2)	0 (0.3)	0	0.06
	1 (0.1)	1	0.02
	2 (0.4)	2	0.08
	3 (0.2)	3	0.04
1 (0.3)	0 (0.3)	1	0.09
	1 (0.1)	2	0.03
	2 (0.4)	3	0.12
	3 (0.2)	4	0.06
2 (0.4)	0 (0.3)	2	0.12
	1 (0.1)	3	0.04
	2 (0.4)	4	0.16
	3 (0.2)	5	0.08
3 (0.1)	0 (0.3)	3	0.03
	1 (0.1)	4	0.01
	2 (0.4)	5	0.04
	3 (0.2)	6	0.02
			1.00

Fig. 7.2: Probability tree presentation of lorry problem

Note how the individual depots' outcomes are combined, each possibility for Firm A's fleet being followed by the four from Firm B, giving 16 in all. Note also how one can check that all possible outcomes *have* been considered. At each 'branching' the sum of the four probabilities equals 1 (since one *or* other of the possible outcomes *must* occur). Note also the final check on all 16 possible mixtures, whose probabilities must similarly equal 1.

7.3 Decision Trees

The idea of 'expected values' can now be applied to Merrion's problem described earlier, relating economic consequences of alternatives to their probability of occurrence.

Further examination of the project proposal yielded the following facts:

a. Economic analysts feel that there is a 20 per cent chance of an economic upturn, 50 per cent of no change, and 30 per cent of a worsening of the economic climate.

b. Developing the infrastructure would cost £1 m., whilst the council would need to spend a further £2 m. if factory units were to be built.

c. The site alone would realise £1.2 m. if sold now. The same figure could be expected if there were to be no significant change in the economy. If there is a downturn, it would sell for only £0.5 m., but if there were to be an upswing, the Council could expect £2.5 m.

d. If the site were developed (in part or full), expected revenues on sale would be:

Climate	Infrastructure only	Infrastructure plus factories built
Upswing	£3 m.	£6 m.
Same	£1.5 m.	£4 m.
Downturn	£0.8 m.	£2 m.

We could now set down all the possible decisions and alternatives outcomes in a diagram. In Fig. 7.3, decision points are denoted by squares, whilst circles denote events which have several (uncertain) outcomes.

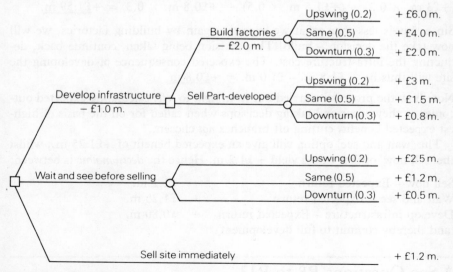

Fig. 7.3: The decision tree

Note how the cost and returns (with appropriate signs) and probabilities have
been incorporated at the appropriate stage of the **decision tree**, and also that
only one decision outcome (sell immediately) has a certain outcome.

We can now look at each outcome in turn, and assess the *expected value*, taking probabilities (risk) into account. Let us examine the 'build factory' option.
The return for each possible outcome can be multiplied by the probability of
that outcome, and the 'expected outcome' calculated. This represents the *average* return that one would expect if the decision to build were implemented
over and over again. The expected profit (or loss) on that stage of the decision
can therefore be assessed by working from right to left. This is shown in
Fig. 7.4.

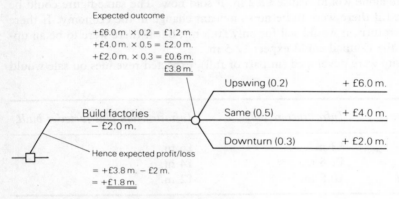

Fig. 7.4: Calculating expected outcomes

In the case of the 'sell part-developed' option, the expected return will be:

$(+£3 \text{ m.} \times 0.2) + (+£1.5 \text{ m.} \times 0.5) + (+£0.8 \text{ m.} \times 0.3) = +\underline{£1.59 \text{ m.}}$

Since this is less than what we expect to gain by building factories, we will
now take the decision – build! This decision being taken, continue back, de-
ducting the infrastructure cost. The expected consequence of developing the
site will thus be + £1.8 m. – £1.0 m. = +£0.8 m.

Note how the process is carried out from *right* to *left*, calculating expected outcomes as they occur and taking decisions when called for on the basis of highest expected benefit, cutting off branches *not* chosen.

The 'wait and see' option will give an expected benefit of +£1.25 m., whilst
the 'sell now' option would yield + £1.2 m. Hence the *decision now* is between:

Sell now – Expected return   +   £1.2 m.
Wait and see – Expected return   +   £1.25 m.
Develop infrastructure – Expected return   +   £0.80 m.
(and thereby commit to full development)

★ See Questions B8 to B13

On the available data, the 'wait and see' option wins by a slender margin. But can the Council afford the risk? Might a certain £1.2 m. now be a better bet than a possible £0.80 m. or £2.5 m. in future? The decision tree approach lays down the options. The decision still lies with managers, and they may or may not be gambling men and women! Note that the expected values are averages only and *not* the final payoffs of the project.

The final decision tree, with all calculations and decisions incorporated, is shown in Fig. 7.5. (Decision options which will *not* be taken are denoted by a pair of lines across the path.)

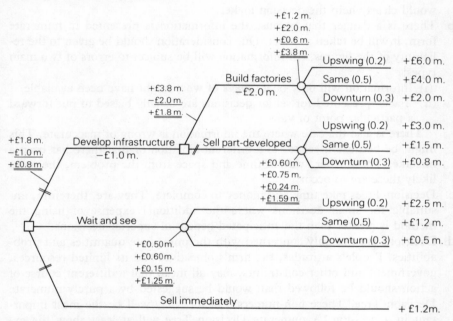

Fig. 7.5: The complete decision tree

As with any numerate technique, decision trees have advantages and disadvantages.

Advantages
  i. By showing clearly the different decisions which could be made, they often throw up new ideas.
 ii. Once the Decision Tree is established, it shows the information which will be needed to reach a decision.
iii. The very use of the Tree encourages quantification, which in itself tends to improve decision making.
 iv. The clarity of layout assists in the planning after the decision has been taken.
  v. The method can easily be combined with other techniques like **discounted cash flow** and **critical path analysis**.

Limitations and Dangers

a. The information may not be available, even when it is known what is required, e.g. if the particular decision has never been taken before, there will be no evidence on which to base the probability of outcomes. Hence, Decision Trees are most easily employed for tactical decisions. Even then care must be taken to see that the total conditions of the new situation really are the same as on previous occasions.

   Sometimes it is possible to draw up a most pessimistic and a most optimistic view. If the same decision were to be reached in both cases, the tree would clearly help the decision maker.

b. There is a danger that because the information is presented in numerate form, it will be taken as exact. Due consideration should be given to the reliability of the figures. All information will be subject to errors of two main types:

   (i) Information will only be a *sample* of what might have been available.

   (ii) 'Facts' presented for senior decisions are usually biased to put forward a particular point of view.

   There is also the case where the information is wrong or inaccurate. This might be because it relates to a different situation or that there has been a mistake. The further away in time and space from the problem, the more likely these are to occur.

c. Decision Trees take time and money to complete. They are, therefore, unsuitable for small decisions where the additional expense of using the method is greater than the anticipated benefit of superior decisions.

d. Decisions are not only concerned with the immediate quantities and probabilities. People's attitudes, the firm's objectives and its limited resources, government and other constraints, may all mean that a different course of action should be followed than would be suggested by a purely numerate Decision Tree. These non-numerate factors may well be the most important in a decision. A numerate Decision Tree will at least show the expected 'numerate opportunity cost' of taking a different alternative than is suggested by the Tree.

   In extreme cases when numerate factors can be seen from the outset to be of secondary importance, the numerate side of Decision Trees should not be followed. The Tree itself, however, might help clarify alternatives.

Work Section

A. Revision Questions

A1 Suggest a formula which might enable one to determine the probability of a particular event occurring.

A2 Why must the sum of probabilities of alternative outcomes in a given situation be 1?

A3 What do you understand by 'mutually exclusive outcomes'?

A4 When would one add probabilities?

A5 When would one multiply probabilities?

A6 What does a probability tree show?

A7 What do you understand by 'expected value'?

A8 When would one use circles or squares in a decision tree?

A9 Briefly outline the sequence of analysing a decision tree.

A10 Give three advantages and three disadvantages of decision trees as a management aid.

B. Exercises/Case Studies

B1 Discuss the following statements:
   a. 'The probability that a student passes a test is 0.8. There are 10 people in our set and the first eight have passed, so the last two have failed.'
   b. 'The probability of a person watching BBC TV News at 9 p.m. is 0.4 whilst that of a person watching ITV's 'News at Ten' is 0.5. The probability of a person watching both is therefore 0.5×0.4 or 0.2.'

B2 An aircraft contains 1 million components. Each has a 0.9999 probability of working perfectly for a year. What is the probability that the aircraft will work perfectly for a year?

B3 Part of a cotton mill consists of a number of similar machines attended by a single operator. The machines work automatically except that every so often a thread breaks and the attendant has to join the loose ends and re-start the machine. In any one-minute interval it may be assumed that the probability that no machine breaks down is 13/20, the probability that one breaks down is 6/20, and the probability that two break down is 1/20.
   a. Suggest on what basis these probabilities may have been assigned.
   b. If it takes the operator 2 minutes to attend to each machine that stops, find what proportion of the time he will be idle.
   c. What is the probability that more than one machine will break down

in any particular two-minute interval so that a machine is temporarily idle and unattended to?

d. Write down an expression for the probability that no machine will break down in a particular ten-minute interval. Do not evaluate your answer.

(Cambridge Local Examinations Syndicate 'A' Level paper)

B4 An activity in a project is composed of three jobs which must be undertaken one after another. For each, there is a probability of $\frac{1}{4}$ that it will take 2 days, of $\frac{1}{2}$ that it will take 3 days, and of $\frac{1}{4}$ that it will take 4 days. Assuming statistical independence, find the probability that the activity will be completed in 6 or 7 days.

B5 On average 5 per cent of the workers in a factory are absent on any one day. What is the probability that someone will be at work for 5 consecutive days?

B6 A machine repair record shows that it is out of service for 10 per cent of the time. If three such machines are installed, what is the probability that:
a. no machines are working;
b. only one machine is working;
c. more than one machine is working.

B7 Three machines, X, Y and Z produce respectively 50 per cent, 30 per cent and 20 per cent of the total number of items produced in a factory. The percentage of defective items made by these machines is, respectively, 3 per cent, 4 per cent and 5 per cent.
a. If an item is selected at random, what is the probability that it is defective?
b. Suppose an item is selected, and is found to be defective, what is the probability that it came from machine X?

B8 *A Party Gamble*
You are at a party and have been asked if you want to take part in the following gamble:
The entrant draws a card from a normal pack. If he gets a heart he will gain £100. If a diamond he loses £24. If a club he loses £40. If a spade he loses £45. *But* if he picks a spade he has the *option* of picking afresh (from a new pack) and he may win £100 if either a heart, diamond or club is drawn whilst he will lose a further £200 if it is a spade for the second time.
i. Would you expect to win if you entered? (Draw, and work through, the appropriate Decision Tree.)
ii. What other reasons might there be for entering or not entering?

B9 *The Production Manager's Decision*
The monthly budgets have just been placed before the production manager of a chemical plant. They show a negative variance of £4,000 in the profit for the responsibility area. This largely results from waste through

bad quality, caused by problems within the semi-automated plant. Such a variance has occurred before and it is known that there is a 75 per cent chance that the system will right itself (however, whether it does or does not, will not be known until the end of the next month and if it has not then another equal sum will be lost).

The manager may act immediately to right any problem but this will mean stripping the plant and closing it for a day. The overall loss in profit is estimated at £600. Assuming that there was something wrong, there would be a 90 per cent chance that the fault was found and the trouble cured; the other 10 per cent of the time the investigation would be to no avail.

If you were the manager, would you act on this numerical information?

B10 *The Investor's Dilemma*

An investor has some money which he wishes to place on the stock market. He knows that he could put it in gilt edge (fixed interest stock) when, after personal taxation, he would gain an income of $3\frac{1}{2}$ per cent and would expect an annual capital gain (after tax) of 2 per cent a year up to maturity of the stock.

An alternative suggestion has come from his stockbroker. He can put the money into ordinary shares of an unusual firm, 'Growth Ltd'. The broker considers that there is a 75 per cent chance of a capital appreciation of 15 per cent a year; on the other hand there is a 25 per cent chance of the shares dropping about 6 per cent a year. No dividend is expected from this company as all profits are ploughed back. (It may be assumed that capital gains tax of $33\frac{1}{3}$ per cent will have to be paid, or will be retrievable in the event of a loss.)

   i. Draw up the Decision Tree to show clearly the alternatives and work out the investor's best course of action.

   ii. What other factors might influence his decision?

B11 *The Oil Wildcatter's Decision*

His job was to go around and drill for oil in a manner which, on the evidence he had, would be most beneficial for Mobul Ltd, his company. He had just arrived in Kulata, a Middle East state, and had the following information from his predecessor:

   'In my experience there are roughly three possibilities if you drill in Kulata. Sixty per cent of the wells will be dry; 30 per cent wet and 10 per cent soaking. The monetary pay off for Mobul from each event, if it occurs, will be minus £70,000 if it is dry; £50,000 if wet; £200,000 if soaking. On appreciating the situation I stopped drilling.'

In the village there was a seismic survey consultant team who were just finishing work for another company. They offered to take seismic soundings at £5,000 a time. They claimed they could show whether there was i. no structure (an unlikely place to find oil); ii. an open cyclical structure (reasonably promising); or iii. a closed cyclical structure (very promising).

The table below shows the probability of each structure existing and the chance there would then be a dry, wet or soaking well, if drilling took place.

	Probability of finding at each seismic survey	*Then*, chance of being dry, wet, soaking, if drilled		
		Dry	Wet	Soaking
No structure	0.2	0.95	0.04	0.01
Open structure	0.6	0.6	0.3	0.1
Closed cyclical structure	0.2	0.2	0.5	0.3

i. Was the Wildcatter's predecessor correct in his decision?
ii. Draw up and quantify a Decision Tree which would allow one to work out if the seismic team should be employed. Then work through the Tree deciding a. what actions you would take at various decision points; b. what benefit or loss would most likely come from employing a seismic team.

B12 *Stygian Chemicals Ltd*

Stygian Chemicals Ltd, is a medium-sized company who has done well to keep its market share in competition with the modern giants. It is always on the alert for a chance to expand when the right opportunity occurs.

Over the last few months it has been considering what plant it should build to produce the new chemical 'SP2'. Technically and for future policy reasons, it is seriously wishing to enter the area, preferably at once. But if it builds a large plant immediately it could prove very expensive if the market subsequently turned out to be small; on the other hand, if it built a small plant the risk would be less and a second plant might be added later if new information then showed it was desirable (but it costs more, both to build and to run, two small plants as against one large one). The following information was available:

Construction costs: There was general agreement from the engineers that the cost of a large plant would be about £3 m. whilst a small plant would only be about £1.3 m. (however, if a second small plant were added later this would cost £2.2 m.).

Market situation: The marketing boys felt that their forecasts should be divided into the short term (first two years) and the long term (up to 10 years from now).

They put it like this:

i. A 60 per cent chance that in the short term there will be a high demand subsequently sustained for the whole period.

ii. A 20 per cent chance that there will be a high demand but after two years it will be clear that demand will be low for the rest of that period.

iii. A 20 per cent chance that there will be a low demand which will remain at that level throughout the period.

Cash Flow: In conjunction with the production team and the accountants, the marketing side then produced the following estimate of cash flow in each eventuality (i.e. sales revenue less all costs except depreciation and construction)

a. Large plant with a high volume of sales   £1 m. p.a.
b. Large plant with a low volume of sales   £100,000 p.a.
c. A small plant with a low volume of sales   £400,000 p.a.
d. A small plant with an initial high demand   £450,000 p.a.
 (but if the high demand continued in the long run this would drop to £300,000 p.a. after year 2 because of competition in the market).
e. If a small plant was expanded to meet sustained high demand the total unit would yield £700,000 p.a. for the eight years remaining (but if a second small plant was built and there was no demand for the last eight years the cash flow would only be £50,000 p.a.).

The whole project should be considered over 10 years, but the cash flow should not be discounted, as would be proper. Also, of course, implicitly assume that one has achieved the state of instant building once a decision is reached.

 i. Construct a Tree diagram which illustrates the alternatives and add relevant numerate data.

 ii. Carefully consider the meaning of the whole and then solve to show the highest expected monetary value that might result from particular decisions.

 iii. What factors, not given, might influence the decision a Board might reach?

B13 A company is considering whether or not to carry out a test market for a product. This would cost £100,000 and would show the strength of the market. Estimates now suggest that there is a 60 per cent chance that the test launch will show strong demand and a 30 per cent chance it will show a satisfactory demand.

 If the test market were to show a strong demand the company would launch nationally using campaign A costing £500,000. If it showed a satisfactory demand it would launch at the same time but with campaign B costing only £300,000. If the demand was unsatisfactory the company would take no further action. Previous launches suggest that if campaign A was used, the company would have a 70 per cent chance of achieving a very successful outcome and a 30 per cent chance of being relatively unsuccessful. On the other hand, if campaign B was used there would be a 90 per cent chance of success and a 10 per cent chance of being unsuccessful. The cash payments and returns from each of the various outcomes mentioned above, is shown below. For some time it has been customary for the company to expect to earn 15 per cent on its financial schemes.

Net cash flows in the eventuality of each alternative occurring (£)

| | Campaign A | | Campaign B | |
	If successful	If unsuccessful	If successful	If unsuccessful
Year 0	−100,000	−100,000	−100,000	−100,000
Year 1	−500,000	−500,000	−300,000	−300,000
Year 2	−200,000	−400,000	−400,000	−100,000
Year 3	+1,400,000	+400,000	+500,000	+200,000
Year 4	+500,000	+100,000	+100,000	—
Total	1,100,000	−500,000	+600,000	−300,000

Question: Ignoring the timing of possible cash inflows and outflows, show whether or not the company should proceed, from this evidence, with the test market.

(Cambridge Local Examinations Syndicate)

C. Essay Qusetions

C1 Discuss three business situations in which a knowledge of probability might be of importance.

C2 How can Decision Trees assist in the process of decision making?

C3 What are the limitations of Decision Trees in business situations?

Chapter 8

Taking Samples (1): The Binomial Distribution

Objectives: *To show how the sampling of discrete variables can be derived from simple probability, and to show how the Poisson approximation may be used in practical applications of sampling (such as quality control) under certain conditions.*

Plan of the chapter:

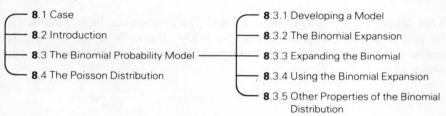

8.1 Case

Merrion Council has five separate departments, each in a separate building, and it is proposed to bring them together. At present, each department has its own switchboard, with one external line. How many outside lines should there be for the combined department? To install a five-line switchboard may be wasteful, yet one with only a single line may be overloaded. On average, each individual line is in use for 20 per cent of the time.

8.2 Introduction

Problems such as this are common in business, especially in areas connected with quality control. The decision maker needs to know how likely a particular outcome occurs, so that he can take the necessary action at an early stage. A key feature to note is that in such cases, there are no alternatives other than 0, 1, 2 . . . etc. lines in use (or free). Fractional values are not possible. Hence the problem is one involving **discrete variables**. (By contrast, a study of adult female heights could yield *any* value, subject only to the accuracy of measurement.)

The telephone problem can be tackled by using the ideas on probability developed in the last chapter.

8.3 The Binomial Probability Model

Each external telephone line can exist in one of only two states. Either it is engaged or free. One or other *must* be true, so we can say:

$$P_{(\text{Eng})} + P_{(\text{Free})} = 1$$

8.3.1 Developing a Model

Let us assume that for 1 line only

The probability of an individual line being engaged $= p$
The probability of an individual line being free $\quad = q$
So $\quad p + q = 1$

What happens if we now consider 2 lines? The position can be summarised in the probability tree diagram of Fig. 8.1 below: For each of the two departments, a line may be either free or engaged, thus giving four possible outcomes.

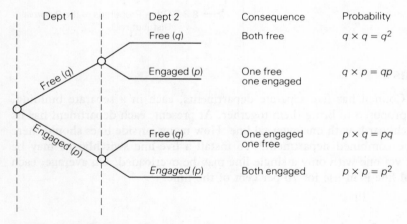

Fig. 8.1: Probability tree for two lines

Since one or other of the four possible consequences *must* happen, we can see that the probabilities of each can be summarised by:

$$p^2 + 2pq + q^2 = 1$$

(Note that in Fig. 8.1, we have assumed statistical independence, which may not be strictly true, since calls are not necessarily uniformly distributed through the day. However, the assumption won't be too far off the mark, and improvements in accuracy may not be worth the extra costs involved.)

What now if 3 lines are considered? Figure 8.2 summarises the position.

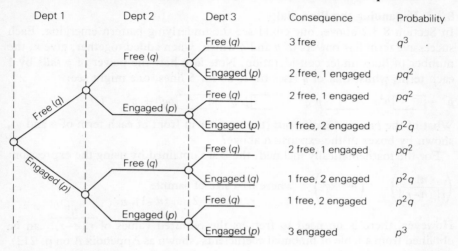

Fig. 8.2: Probability tree for three lines

Once again, one or other consequence will occur, so the probabilities of each outcome can be summarised as:

$$p^3 + 3p^2q + 3pq^2 + q^3 = 1$$

If we consider the situation for 4 and 5 lines do we *have* to go through the tree diagram in each case? If we *do*, the prospect of a twenty-line exchange is horrifying!

8.3.2 The Binomial Expansion
Let us now look at the position so far:

No. of lines	Probability given by:
1	$p + q = 1$
2	$p^2 + 2pq + q^2 = 1$
3	$p^3 + 3p^2q + 3pq^2 + q^3 = 1$

There seems to be a pattern here.

In fact, the probability expressions are linked by the binomial:

$$(p + q)^n = 1 \qquad \text{where } n = 1, 2, 3, \ldots \text{etc.}$$

(The name binomial comes from the fact that there are two numbers involved, here p and q.)

So the situation for 5 lines should be given by the expansion of the expression for $n = 5$:

$$(p + q)^5 = 1$$

8.3.3 Expanding the Binomial

In Section 8.3.2 above, one could see the underlying pattern emerging. Each successive term has powers of p and q which, when added together, give n, the number of lines under consideration. Note also how the power of p falls by 1 each term, whilst that of q rises by 1. So for 5 lines, one might see:

$$p^5 + \boxed{}p^4q + \boxed{}p^3q^2 + \boxed{}p^2q^3 + \boxed{}pq^4 + q^5 = 1.$$

What of the *binomial coefficients* (the number in front of each term of p and q), shown by boxes in the expansion above?

For the mathematically inclined, these are obtained by using the expression:

$$\left(\frac{n!}{r!\,(n-r)!}\right) \times \left(p^{(n-r)}q^r\right) \quad \text{where } n = \text{size of sample}$$
$$r = 0, 1, 2 \ldots (n-1), n.$$

However, there is no need to fret, as the required values of $\frac{n!}{r!(n-r)!}$ can be obtained from a table of binomial coefficients (shown as Appendix A on p. 213). From this, taking the row for $n = 5$, we have:

r:	0	1	2	3	4	5
$n = 5$:	1	5	10	10	5	1

and inserting these into the spaces of the earlier expression gives:

$$p^5 + 5p^4q + 10p^3q^2 + 10p^2q^3 + 5pq^4 + q^5 = 1.$$

Hence the binomial expansion for *any* value of n can now be produced if needed.

8.3.4 Using the Binomial Expansion

Having survived the maths, one may be tempted to ask 'so what?'. The answer is that *successive terms of the binomial give the probabilities of each discrete event*. So for our 5 line case:

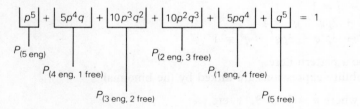

In our example, we found that the probability of an individual line being used was 0.2 (or 20 per cent of the time). So $p = 0.2$, and hence $q = 0.8$, since $p + q = 1$.

Substituting these values into the expression, we obtain:

No. of lines in use	Probability expression	Probability		
5	p^5	$(0.2)^5$	=	0.00032
4	$5p^4q$	$5(0.2)^4(0.8)$	=	0.00640
3	$10p^3q^2$	$10(0.2)^3(0.8)^2$	=	0.05120
2	$10p^2q^3$	$10(0.2)^2(0.8)^3$	=	0.20480
1	$5p\,q^4$	$5(0.2)\,(0.8)^4$	=	0.40960
0	q^5	$(0.8)^5$	=	0.32768
				1.00000

The probability distribution of events is shown in Figure 8.3

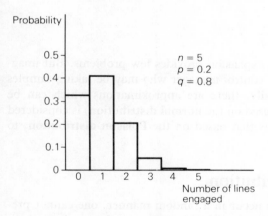

Fig. 8.3: Probability distribution for five lines

From this information, we can see that five lines in simultaneous use will occur on average on only three occasions in ten thousand; *not* very likely, so to install a five-line exchange would be a waste of money.

The probability of four or more lines would be $(0.00032 + 0.00640) = 0.00672$; again, not very likely.

Even three or more in use would only have a probability of $(0.0032 + 0.0064 + 0.05120) = 0.05792$, so a *two* line exchange would cover over 94 per cent of occasions. Can the cost of extra lines be justified by the benefits obtained?

There may even be a case for just *one* line.

To summarise:

a. In order to use the binomial, individual events can only occur in one of two

ways, whose probabilities are p and q. These probabilities must remain constant throughout (so implying a large population).
  b. For a sample of n items at a time, the probabilities of the possible outcomes are given by the successive terms of the binomial $(p + q)^n = 1$.
  c. Produce the terms expansion by using the general expression

$$\left(\frac{n!}{r!(n-r)!}\right) \times \left(p^{(n-r)} q^r\right) \text{ where } r = 0, 1, 2 \ldots (n-1), n.$$

  d. Substituting values of p and q into each successive term gives the probability of each possible outcome.

8.3.5 Other Properties of the Binomial Distribution

The distribution obtained in Fig. 8.3 has a mean and standard deviation just like any other frequency distribution. In the example, if a line is engaged on average for 0.2 of the time, then on average (0.2×5) of the five lines will be engaged. (Note that this *could* be a fractional value; it is only an average. After all, who ever met Mr. and Mrs. Joe Average and their 2.2 children!)

For a binomial distribution for a sample of n items, with probabilities of p and q:

The mean $= n.p$
The standard deviation $= \sqrt{n.p.q.}$

For small samples, the binomial expansion provides few problems. But imagine the problem facing a quality control manager who may be taking samples of several hundred items! Luckily, there are approximations which can be used in certain cases, and one (based on the **normal distribution**) is considered in Chapters 9 and 10. Another is that based on the **Poisson distribution**, to which we now turn.

8.4 The Poisson Distribution

In many situations where events occur in a random manner, one cannot predict precisely when an event will occur. Neither can one foresee how many events will occur together. The arrivals of aircraft at a large airport after long journeys or the number of defective screws in a box are typical examples.

But we *can* say something about the average pattern of events over a long period. So a school may experience an average of 1.3 broken limbs during a year's athletics training. How likely is it to experience 0, 1, 2, 3 etc. broken limbs?

The Poisson formula:

$$P_{(x)} = \frac{e^{-a} \times a^x}{x!}$$ where $x!$ (pronounced 'x factorial') $= x \times (x - 1) \ldots \times 2 \times 1$
a = mean no. of events
x = no. of events required
e is the 'exponent' (a constant 2.719)

allows one to determine such values. (The underlying maths is quite complex, so please accept the formula on trust.)

So for no fractures p.a., we have $a = 1.3$ and $x = 0$ and hence:

$$P_{(0)} = \frac{e^{-1.3} \times (1.3)^0}{(0)!}$$

But since $(1.3)^0 = 1$ and $(0)! = 1$ (surprising, but true)

$$P_{(0)} = e^{-1.3}$$
$$= \underline{0.273}$$

Thus one expects no breakages p.a. to have a probability of 0.273.
One fracture p.a. would have a probability of:

$$\frac{e^{-1.3} \times (1.3)^1}{(2)!} = \underline{0.230}$$

and so on for 3, 4, 5 etc. fractures p.a. Note that there is no theoretical maximum to the number of fractures that might occur. However, low probabilities soon result.

In order to use the Poisson distribution as an approximation to the binomial the following must be observed:

n (the sample size) is large (greater than about 20)
np is small (typically less than 7 or 8)
p is small (less than about 0.1) *or* large (greater than about 0.9)

The approximation improves as each factor becomes very large or very small as appropriate.

Under such conditions, one can take

$a = np$

as the approximate mean to use in the Poisson formula.

Example 1: On average 2 per cent of capacitors produced on a particular machine are defective. If a sample of 200 capacitors is taken, what is the probability of finding at least one defective?

In this case, the three conditions are met, so we can use the Poisson approximation to the binomial where:

$a = np = 200 \times 0.02 = 4$
$P_{(at\ least\ 1\ def)} = 1 - P_{(0\ def)}$
and $P_{(0\ def)} = \dfrac{e^{-4} \times 4^0}{0!} = e^{-4} = \underline{0.018}$

So the probability of finding one or more defectives is $(1 - 0.018) = \underline{0.982}$, which is therefore very likely.

Example 2: Suppose the same sampling process reveals 10 defective in a sample of 200. What would you conclude?

The probability of 10 defective occurring is given by:

$$P_{(10\ def)} = \frac{e^{-4} \times 4^{10}}{10!} = \underline{0.0053}$$

In other words, the result is a very rare chance event, or (more likely) the process was producing more than 2 per cent defective products.

Work Section

A. Revision Questions

A1 What are discrete variables?

A2 Give two examples of discrete variables.

A3 What is the general formula for a binomial of n items, having probabilities p and q?

A4 Write out the binomial expansion for $n = 6$.

A5 What does each term of the binomial tell us if values are substituted for letters?

A6 Write an expression which gives the mean of a binomial.

A7 Write an expression which gives the standard deviation of a binomial.

A8 Write down an expression for the Poisson probability of an event.

A9 What three conditions must be met before the Poisson distribution can be used as an approximation to the binomial?

A10 Give two examples of situations in which Poisson may be used as an approximation to the binomial.

B. Exercises/Case Studies

B1 Find the probability that at any instant 0, 1, 2 telephone lines are free if they are used for a. 30 per cent of their time; b. 40 per cent of their time, when there are two lines available.

B2 Calculate the probability that two or more lines are engaged out of three when each is used on average for 30 per cent of its time.

B3 Using the same figures as in B2 calculate whether a 40 per cent success rate in calls would have been justified.

B4 In a large company 40 per cent of the employees are men and 60 per cent are women. Each employee automatically enters for the Xmas 'draw' in which there are 8 prizes. What is the probability that the prizes will be awarded to 3 men and 5 women?

B5 Using the same figures as for B4, is the answer you obtain the same as the probability of finding 3 men and 5 women on a particular table seating 8 at the canteen. If yes, why? If not, why not?

B6 A check in a shoe factory showed two shoes with imperfect stitching in a sample of 10. What is the probability of a sample yielding 0, 1 and 2 defectives if 10 per cent of all shoes are defective?

B7 It is expected that 5 per cent of the production from a continuous process will be defective and scrapped. Determine the probability that in a sample of 10 units chosen at random that: a. exactly two will be defective; b. at least two will be defective.

B8   A shop will accept batches of goods from a supplier if either of the following conditions is fulfilled:

   i. A random sample of 6 articles shows none defective.

   ii. The first sample contains 1 or 2 defectives, but a second sample shows none.

   If these conditions are not met, then the batch is scrapped.

   a. What chance is there of a batch being accepted if a 10 per cent defective level exists?

   b. What criteria would you employ to decide whether this is a good method of acceptance sampling compared with others?

B9   A customer is buying a large consignment of nails from a manufacturer. To test the quality of the nails, he takes a sample of 100, and if he finds fewer than 2 blunt ones, he accepts delivery. What are the chances of a batch being accepted if:

   a. The consignment contains no blunt nails?

   b. The consignment contains 1 per cent blunt?

   c. The consignment contains 2 per cent blunt?
       Use the binomial distribution for parts a to c.

   d. What production standards should the producers aim at if they wish to be 95 per cent certain of the customer accepting the consignment?

B10 Use the Poisson approximation to estimate values for b. and c. in Question B9 above.

B11 On average, a ten-roomed hotel has 4.6 rooms occupied. How often would it expect to have to turn away guests because all rooms are occupied? How often would it expect to be completely empty?

B12 On average, a factory switchboard receives three calls in every 15 minutes. To carry out routine maintenance, it is necessary to close the switchboard for half an hour. What is the probability that no incoming calls will be lost?

B13 A teacher is interrupted on average twice each lunchtime by students having trouble with statistics. How often can she expect to get an uninterrupted lunch break?

B14 Design a classroom experiment to show that the binomial distribution does indeed predict the results obtained in practice.

C. Essay Questions

C1   Discuss three situations in which a knowledge of the binomial and Poisson distributions could result in a firm saving money.

C2   Explain to a sceptical, innumerate friend how it is possible to predict in advance what might occur when one takes samples.

Chapter 9

Taking Samples (2): The Normal Distribution

Objectives: *To show how many different distributions may be linked via the use of the standardised Normal Distribution, and to show how this may be used as an approximation to the binomial.*

Plan of the chapter:

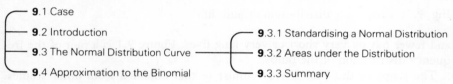

9.1 Case

Merrion Council is soon to debate whether Merrion Broadway ought to become a traffic-free shopping area. The Council decided to commission a survey of public opinion. Out of a random sample of 200 shoppers, 108 supported the move and 92 opposed it. Is this evidence of a clear majority in favour of the proposal? Such problems involving the significance of results occurs in all organisations, even schools (as we saw in Ch. 1). Other fields include market research, opinion polls and attitude surveys.

9.2 Introduction

A the end of the previous chapter we noted that once the size of samples increased, the binomial probability model becomes unwieldy. Samples of several hundred are by no means uncommon in quality control of high volume processes. Evaluating even the first few terms of something like $(p + q)^{200} = 1$ would be a fearsome operation. Luckily, there are approximations which relieve us of such a task.

Let us return to the problem of Sparklight lightbulbs considered earlier. Whilst the mean life of 100 bulbs in the sample was 699.7 hr, the lives are spread about this figure. Most bulbs have lives close to the mean, with fewer

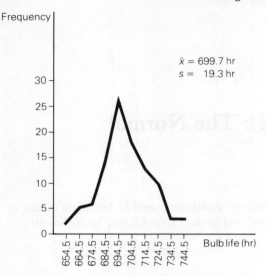

Fig. 9.1: Frequency distribution of bulb life

and fewer having very short or very long lives. Figure 9.1 is a plot of the frequency distribution of the bulbs.

The shape of this plot is very similar to that obtained from other studies. ★ Large samples of adult male heights, I.Q. results, product dimension or adult female weights would show similar shapes. In particular, the plots are,
- Symmetrical about the mean, median and mode values.
- Bell-shaped, with a distinct point of inflexion on each side of the mean.
Further examination would also reveal that:
- The **points of inflexion** lie at values which correspond to those lying one standard deviation either side of the mean.
- The width of the base of the curve is approximately six standard deviations.
Although quite different units of measurement have been used, the curves seem to have a common relationship. They are all **Normal distributions** (sometimes called Gaussian distributions after Gauss, who did much of the work on its properties).

9.3 The Normal Distribution Curve

Unlike the binomial, Normal distributions are continuous distributions, in that any value of height, weight, I.Q. or bulb life can be obtained. There is little point in trying to compare directly distributions measured in dissimilar units, but comparison *is* possible if we **standardise** them.

★ See Questions B1, B2

9.3.1 **Standardising a Normal Distribution**

This is done in two steps. Firstly, instead of considering the individual hours, I.Q.'s, heights or weights along the x-axis, let us consider their *deviations* from the mean value. Thus for a distribution having a mean value of $\bar{x}$, a value x has a deviation $(x - \bar{x})$ from the mean. But this deviation is still measured in the original units. The second step involves dividing the deviation $(x - \bar{x})$ by the standard deviation of the sample (s) to rid us of the original scale units, leaving a dimensionless number for the deviation.

The deviation of a particular value from the mean is therefore now given by the **z-value**, where:

$$z = \frac{(x - \bar{x})}{s}$$

In doing this, we can plot quite dissimilar distribution scales on a common basis, as shown in Fig. 9.2.

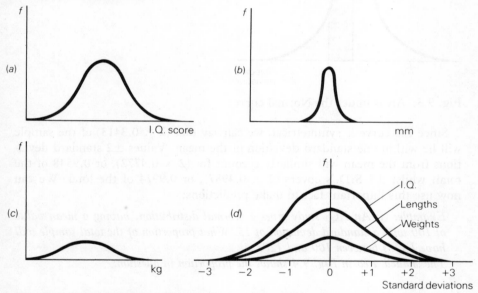

Fig. 9.2: Combining (a) I.Q. results (b) Product lengths (c) Female weights (d) By using a common S.D. scale

> *Example: i. The Sparklight data produced a mean life ($\bar{x}$) of 699.7 hr with a standard deviation of 19.3 hr (s). A life of 719 hr (x) is therefore:*

$$z = \frac{719.0 - 699.7}{19.3} = +\underline{1.0} \text{ S.D.'s from the mean.}$$

> *ii. An I.Q. test has a mean of 100 and a standard deviation of 15. Hence an I.Q. of 115 lies:*

$$z = \frac{115 - 100}{15} = +\underline{1.0} \text{ S.D.'s from mean.}$$

9.3.2 Areas under the Distribution

Since the area under the curve is proportional to the sample size, the area between any two values is proportional to the fraction of the sample bounded by these limits. Luckily, the proportion falling between the mean and a particular value is constant *provided that the deviation of the value is measured in terms of z* (i.e., in terms of standard deviations).

Mathematicians have compiled tables of such values and an example appears at Appendix B. From such tables, one can see that the proportion lying between the mean and a point 1 standard deviation away (i.e. $z = 1.0$) will always be 0.3413. Figure 9.3 illustrates this.

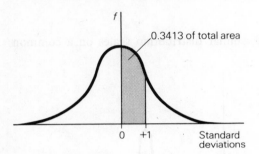

Fig. 9.3: Areas under the Normal curve

Since the curve is symmetrical, we can say that (2×0.3413) of the sample will lie within one standard deviation of the mean. Values ±2 standard deviations from the mean will similarly account for (2×0.4772), or 0.9548 of the total, whilst ±3 S.D.'s covers (2×0.4987), or 0.9974 of the total. We can now use this important fact to make predictions:

Example: (i) An I.Q. study gives a Normal distribution, having a mean value of 100 with a standard deviation of 15. What proportion of the total sample will have I.Q.'s between 100 and 120?
The shaded area in Fig. 9.4 shows the proportion in question:

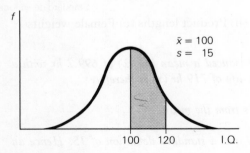

Fig. 9.4: I.Q. distribution

★ See Question B3

Here $z = \dfrac{x - \bar{x}}{s}$

$= \dfrac{120 - 100}{15}$

$= \dfrac{20}{15} = \underline{1.33}$

From Appendix B, the proportion between the mean ($z = 0$) and $z = 1.33$ is 0.4082. Hence 0.4082 of the sample will lie between the stated values.

Example: (ii) A peanut packing machine produces a Normally distributed sample of pack weights, having a mean of 30 g and a standard deviation of 5 g. What proportion of packs will be heavier than 40 g?

Figure 9.5 shows the position.

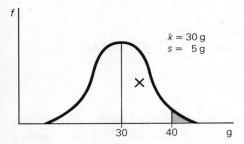

$\bar{x} = 30\,g$
$s = 5\,g$

Fig. 9.5: Peanut packs

40 g has a z-value of $\dfrac{40 - 30}{5} = \underline{2.00}$.

However, the tables give the proportion lying between the mean and a particular z-value (i.e. the area marked X in Fig. 9.5). For $z = 2.00$, this is 0.4772. Since the curve is symmetrical, the proportion above 30 g is half of the total, and hence the required proportion is

$(0.5000 - 0.4772) = \underline{0.0228}$

Example: (iii) What proportion of the sample of Sparklight bulbs will have lives between 720 and 730 hr?
($\bar{x} = 699.7$ and $s = 19.3$).
Figure 9.6 shows the position.

This must be done in two parts:
a. Calculate the proportion lying between the mean and 730 hr; and then
b. Subtract the proportion lying between the mean and 720 hr.

For 730 hr: $z = \dfrac{730 - 699.7}{19.3} = \underline{1.57}$

From the tables, the proportion of the sample lying between the mean and 730 hr is therefore $\underline{0.4418}$

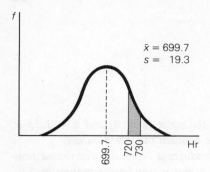

Fig. 9.6: Sparklight bulbs

For 720 hr: $z = \dfrac{720 - 699.7}{19.3} = \underline{1.05}$

From the tables, the sample proportion is $\underline{0.3531}$.
Hence the proportion having lives between 720 and 730 hr will be:

$(0.4418 - 0.3531) = \underline{0.0887}$

9.3.3 Summary

a. Many observations produce frequency distributions of similar shape, being symmetrical and bell-shaped, with points of inflexion lying one standard deviation either side of the mean value. Mean, median and mode coincide.

b. All such distribution are examples of Normally distributed data.

c. All are linked by the process of 'standardising' the distribution. That is, expressing values in terms of the number of standard deviations from the mean rather than the original units of measurement.

d. Standardising a value (x) is done by calculating z

$z = \dfrac{x - \bar{x}}{s}$ where $\bar{x}$ is the mean value of the sample
s is the standard deviation of the sample.

e. For standardised Normal distributions, the proportion of the total sample lying between the mean and a particular z-value is constant, and can be found by reference to standard tables.

9.4 Approximation to the Binomial

In Chapter 8 we saw how, in certain specified circumstances, the tedious business of evaluating the binomial could be eased by taking an approximation, the

---

★ See Questions B4 to B11

Poisson distribution. In the same way, the Normal distribution can be used to approximate, but only if the binomial has the following characteristics:

p lies between 0.1 and 0.9
np is larger than about 5

(Compare these assumptions with those for the Poisson approximation in Chapter 8.)

We began the chapter by posing a question in relation to a survey of public opinion commissioned by Merrion Council. The results of the survey of a random sample of 200 people was that 108 supported the move and 92 were against having a traffic-free shopping area. We wish to calculate the probability of up to 108 people being in favour, on the assumption that complete indifference would give a probability of 0.5 for both p and q.

In this case, we now have:
$n = 200$
$p = 0.5$
$q = 0.5$ and hence the mean ($\bar{x}$) is $n.p = (200 \times 0.5) = \underline{100}$

The conditions for the Normal approximation to the binomial thus apply. But we need both mean *and* standard deviation figures to work with a Normal distribution. Section **8.3.5** gave the formula for this:

$$s = \sqrt{npq}$$

So in the Merrion example,

$$s = \sqrt{200 \times 0.5 \times 0.5}$$
$$= \sqrt{50} \quad = \underline{7.07}.$$

Figure 9.7 now shows the Normal model approximating to the binomial

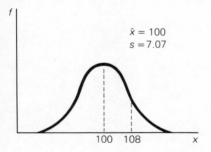

$\bar{x} = 100$
$s = 7.07$

100   108 x

Fig. 9.7: Normal approximation to the binomial

The observed result (x) is 108 people wanting the traffic-free area and the z-value is

$$z = \frac{108 - 100}{7.07} = 1.13.$$

What $z = 1.13$ implies is that the observation of 108 is just over 1 standard deviation above the arithmetic mean – one standard deviation on either side of the arithmetic mean is not an unusual event (about 1 in 3). More than 2 standard deviations is rare (about 1 in 20). More than 3 standard deviations above or below the arithmetic mean is exceptional (about 3 in 1,000).

Thus we can conclude that an observation of 108 in a sample of 200 would not be an unusual event and would not provide evidence that the majority of the population are in favour of a traffic-free shopping area.

You will agree that this is rather quicker than evaluating the terms of the binomial $(0.5 + 0.5)^{200} = 1$.

★ It may be worth pausing to remind ourselves what Fig. 9.7 shows. It is the probability distribution obtained from taking a large number of samples of 200. On *average*, we would expect to get a result of 100 people wanting a traffic-free zone, but lesser or greater results *could* occur, although these are less likely.

The example also serves to illustrate the idea of **significance testing**. We have asked whether a particular result is likely to occur merely as a result of the inherent unpredictability of sampling. The next chapter now looks at problems such as this in more detail.

★ See Question B12

Work Section

A. Revision Questions

A1 What is continuous distribution?

A2 What are the general features of a Normal curve?

A3 Which two measures determine the shape and position of the Normal curve?

A4 Why does one standardise a Normal distribution?

A5 Give a formula for calculating z and briefly say what it tells you.

A6 Describe how you would use the Normal distribution:
   a. Determine the proportion of observation lying above the given value.
   b. Determine the proportion of observation lying between two values.

A7 What proportion of a Normally distributed population lies:
   a. Within $z = \pm 1$ from mean.
   b. Within $z = \pm 2$ from mean.
   c. Within $z = \pm 3$ from mean.

A8 What are the z-values which correspond to the following probability figures: 0.5544, 0.4974, 0.1000, 0.2500?

A9 When using the Normal curve as an approximation to the binomial distribution, what conditions must be met?

A10 How would you find the mean and standard deviation of a Normal approximation of the binomial?

B. Exercises/Case Studies

B1 Construct a histogram, and approximate with a frequency polygon, of the heights of 50 of your fellow students. How would you describe the shape of your distribution? If it is 'Normal', why? If not, why not?

B2

(a) Heights of Italian males

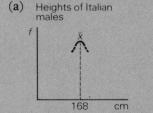

(b) Heights of Norwegian males

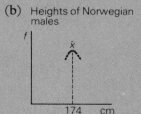

   a. Why can't you complete the two diagrams above?
   b. Make an attempt to draw the diagram if the standard deviation of the

heights of Italian men and Norwegian men are 5 and 10 cm respectively.

B3   Use tables to find the probability that correspond to the z-values below:

a. $z > 0.4$ d. $z < 1.4$

b. $z < 1.0$ e. $0.4 < z < 1.0$

c. $z > 2.5$ f. $-1.4 > z > 2.5$

B4   The average annual earnings of a group of 10,000 unskilled engineering workers is £4,000 with a standard deviation of £800. Assuming that the earnings were Normally distributed, find how many workers earned:

a. less than £4,000;

b. more than £2,400 but less than £3,200;

c. more than £4,000 but less than £4,800;

d. above £4,800.

B5   The completed length of service of typists in an office typing pool is an average of 345 days with a standard deviation of 80 days. Assuming a Normal distribution of completed length of service, obtain:

a. the percentage of typists who have completed more than 400 days;

b. the value above which we would find the 25 per cent longest serving typists;

c. the proportion of typists who have completed between 150 and 450 working days.

B6   An instant-coffee manufacturer wishes to set his filling machine so that on average only 1 jar in 100 is filled with less than the nominal 500 g. If the variability of the contents, based on previous experience, is a standard deviation of 12 g, by what amount should the manufacturer overfill his jars on average? Assume a Normal distribution.

B7   The number of arrivals at a supermarket between 9 a.m. and 9.30 a.m. has a mean of 230 and a standard deviation of 20. On what percentage of occasions will there be between 200 and 250 arrivals during this period? Assume a Normal distribution.

B8   A meat importer prepares fillet steak for sale at supermarkets. It is very difficult to control the variation in the weight of the steaks cut by an automatic slicer, and so in order to obviate the cost of individual weighing and pricing, the importer labels all steaks with the same price and offers a £1 'compensation bonus to any purchaser who finds that the weight of the steak falls short of 8 oz.' (The steak has to be returned and cannot be used again.)

During a previous month of production, tests were carried out where all steaks cut in that month were weighed and their packaging marked. The results were Normally distributed with a mean weight of 5.0 oz. and a standard deviation of 0.50 oz. The company also found that 0.3 per cent of that month's output was returned to customers.

a. What proportion could have been returned?

b. What proportion were returned out of those eligible for return?

    c. If the production costs per steak of x ounces is $(2x + 5)$ pence, evaluate the total expected cost per steak (including the expected compensation bonus) for steaks of an average weight of 8 oz, 8.5 oz, and 9 oz. You may assume that the standard deviation remains at 0.5 oz throughout.

B9 A product has been designed with a diameter of 50.00 mm and a tolerance on this of $\pm$ 0.50 mm. Components outside this range will be rejected at a net loss to the company of 5p. The machine can be set to produce components of average diameter 50.0 mm with a standard deviation of 0.4 mm.

    The firm is contemplating the purchase of a new machine which will produce components of the required average diameter, but with a standard deviation of only 0.25 mm. The net purchase price of the new machine would be £1,000 and maintenance costs for the new machine will be an additional £5 per 1,000 components produced. All other operating costs remain the same.

    How many *acceptable* components would have to be produced in order to justify buying the new machine?

B10 The weekly production of a small factory making electric typewriters was recorded for each of the last 50 full working weeks.

    The results were:

Production	10	12	13	14	15	16	17	18
Number of weeks	3	5	7	8	10	9	6	2

    a. Calculate the mean weekly output.

    b. The standard deviation of this sample is 2 (you are not required to verify this). Calculate the probability of an output of 17 or more typewriters in a week using a Normal model with mean and standard deviation equal to those of the given data.

    c. Discuss briefly whether a Normal model is appropriate in this situation.

(Cambridge Local Examinations Syndicate A Level Examination)

B11 A factory complex has a total of 2,000 tubular lights, and the tubes have an average useful life of 3,000 hr, with a standard deviation of 600 hr, following the shape of the Normal distribution. Each light is switched on for an average of 1,000 hr per year. Replacement tubes cost £2 each.

    Under the present system of maintenance, an internal electrician is summoned, when required, to replace a faulty tube. Such a visit costs £2 per tube, in addition to the cost of the tube itself.

    It is suggested that a routine replacement programme should be introduced, by which each tube is replaced in strict rotation, whether finished or not, in such a way as to replace all tubes over a period of two years. This routine fitting would cost only 25 pence per tube (in addition to material cost). If a tube ceases to operate before it is replaced, an outside electrician will be called in, at a cost of £2.25 per tube (in addition to material cost).

a. Calculate which scheme would be cheaper in the long run, and by how much.
b. Outline any further advantages, or disadvantages of the scheme you choose, apart from the cost elements already dealt with in a.

(Cambridge Local Examinations Syndicate A Level Examination)

B12 The managing director of a company manufacturing washing up liquid is concerned about the familiarity of housewives with its brand name 'Ozo'. If less than 70 per cent of all housewives recognise the name, he thinks he should launch a major TV advertising campaign.

The market research department of the company selects a random sample of 200 housewives and asks them, 'With what do you associate Ozo?' 144 housewives correctly identify the name.

a. Discuss whether the managing director should be satisfied with the result.
b. The market research department repeats the survey this time with a larger sample of 1,000 housewives. How many housewives would now have to recognise the name in order to provide satisfactory evidence that no major advertising campaign is necessary?

(Cambridge Local Examinations Syndicate A Level Examination)

C. Essay Questions

C1 Discuss in detail two situations which are likely to provide you with data that conform to a Normal distribution.

C2 'The Normal distribution provides one of the most useful of statistical tools.' Discuss.

C3 A manufacturer of electric light bulbs is considering giving a guarantee with each bulb, i.e. he will offer a free bulb for every one that fails within 2,000 hr. Discuss the statistical and other considerations which should affect his decision.

(Cambridge Local Examinations A Level)

C4 Of what is standard deviation a measure? Give three examples (in contexts as different as possible) where it would be useful to know the standard deviation of a set of observations.

Chapter 10

Using the Normal Distribution

Objectives: *To show how a knowledge of sampling theory can be used to estimate the accuracy of information gained from sample data.*

Plan of the chapter:

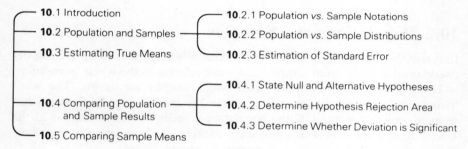

10.1 Introduction

10.2 Population and Samples

10.3 Estimating True Means

10.4 Comparing Population and Sample Results

10.5 Comparing Sample Means

10.2.1 Population *vs.* Sample Notations

10.2.2 Population *vs.* Sample Distributions

10.2.3 Estimation of Standard Error

10.4.1 State Null and Alternative Hypotheses

10.4.2 Determine Hypothesis Rejection Area

10.4.3 Determine Whether Deviation is Significant

10.1 Introduction

The moment that one takes samples, the inevitable question raised is whether or not the results obtained are significant. Do they *actually* show what they are thought to show? On the answer to such a question might lie the fate of a £1 m. advertising campaign or the fate of a party at election time. To answer the question, one needs to assess the statistical significance of sample results. This chapter attempts to look at problems which are likely to be met in many problem areas, from the business studies' student carrying out a survey as part of a project, to a teacher agonising over the most recent set of exam results, to the manager in charge of a market research project.

Because this chapter will inevitably be 'bitty' in character, it is worth setting out what it is intended to cover. If at any stage you get lost, return to this section for re-direction. Questions have been inserted in the text to help you stay on course.

Firstly, it looks at the theoretical way in which the scatter of mean values obtained from samples is related to the true mean of the population from which the samples have been taken (Sections **10.2.1** and **10.2.2**).

Secondly, it shows how one can modify this theory to the practical case of taking large samples, i.e. sample sizes greater than about 30 (Section **10.2.3**).

The chapter then describes a number of practical applications of this theoretical base. In Section **10.3**, the problem is the accuracy with which one can estimate properties of a population knowing only the information gained from sampling. Section **10.4** considers the problem of whether or not a particular sampling result could or could not have come from a specified population (and therefore introduces the idea of *significance testing*).

Finally, Section **10.5** considers problems in which we know nothing about the population themselves, but only have sample results to compare. Could these have come from the *same* population (and differ only because of sampling errors) or do they suggest that they have come from quite different populations?

10.2 Populations and Samples

In discussing statistical significance, it is crucially important to distinguish between results drawn from samples and those relating to the whole population.

The *population* is the totality from which *samples* are drawn. The word 'population' need not be taken literally. In the case of a study of, say, adult women's weights in the UK the population is indeed all adult females in the UK. But in a study of weights of crisp packets, the population is the whole output of a particular machine or department under review.

10.2.1 Population vs. Sample Notations
To ensure that we differentiate between population and sample characteristics, we must use a suitable notation. In the rest of the chapter, we will use the following:

Measure	Population	Sample
Mean	μ	$\bar{x}$
Standard deviation	σ	s
Sample size	–	n

(The Greek symbols μ and σ are pronounced 'mu' and 'sigma' respectively.)

10.2.2 Population vs. Sample Distributions
Suppose that we were interested in the I.Q.'s of 18-year olds in the UK. By definition, the population mean I.Q. is μ, and the standard deviation is σ. Assume that $\mu = 100$. What happens if we take samples of 200 such students?

Common sense tells us that not *every* such sample will have a mean value ($\bar{x}$) of 100. Rather, the sample means will be scattered about the population (or true) mean, and it comes as no surprise to learn that they are distributed in a Normal manner. Figure 10.1 shows this (but note that the vertical scales for population and sample distributions are quite different).

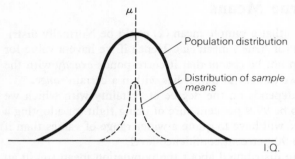

Fig. 10.1: Comparison of population and sample mean distribution

Pause for breath: Are you quite certain what the two distributions in Fig. 10.1 show?

It can be shown that:

a. For a Normally distributed population of mean μ and standard deviation σ the sample means are also Normally distributed, with a mean value μ and a standard deviation of $\sigma/\sqrt{n}$, where n is the size of the samples.

b. For any large population of mean μ and standard deviation σ, the sample means are *approximately* Normally distributed, with mean μ and standard deviation $\sigma/\sqrt{n}$, *as long as the sample size is greater than about $n = 30$*. The approximation improves as sample size increases. For *small samples* ($n < 30$) special techniques are necessary, which are outside the scope of this book.

The standard deviation of sample means about the true population mean is called the **standard error** ($S.E.$) *of the mean.*

Pause for breath: Are you clear on the distinction between the population *standard deviation* (σ) and the *standard error*?

10.2.3 Estimation of Standard Error

In the real life situation, it is most unlikely that we will know the *true* mean (μ) and standard deviation (σ) of the population for the formulae in Section **10.2.2** above. Indeed, we may well be trying to estimate them. A further approximation is needed, which depends on the size of the samples being considered (n). *If n is large ($\geqslant 30$) the population standard deviation (σ) can be replaced by that of the sample (s).*

Pause for breath: Can you see why we must make the above approximation?

Combining the contents of **10.2.2** and **10.2.3** therefore gives us:

Sample size   Approximation of standard error
$n \geqslant 30$ $s/\sqrt{n}$

Let us now see how the standard error might be applied to practical cases.

10.3 Estimating True Means

We saw from Section **10.2.2** that a sample mean ($\bar{x}$) could be Normally distributed about the population (or 'true') mean (μ). Hence if we have a value for the sample mean ($\bar{x}$) we can not be *certain* that it corresponds *exactly* with the population mean. All that we *can* say is that it lies within a certain *range*.

The width of the range depends on the degree of certainty with which we require the answer. Thus to be 99.9 per cent sure of being right (or adopting a *confidence level* of 99.9%) we will have to quote a wider range of values than if we are prepared to accept a 90 per cent confidence level.

Because sample means are distributed about the population mean (μ) in an approximately Normal manner (Section **10.2.2**) we can use the area under the curve to establish the range of values consistent with a given confidence level. Thus the population mean will lie within the range:

$\bar{x} \pm 1.00$ S.E.'s to cover 68 per cent of all possibilities (i.e. a confidence level of 68%)

$\bar{x} \pm 1.96$ S.E.'s to cover 95 per cent of all possibilities (i.e. a confidence level of 95%)

$\bar{x} \pm 2.58$ S.E.'s to cover 99 per cent of all possibilities (i.e. a confidence level of 99%)

Note how the range of possible values increases as the desired confidence level increases.

Pause for breath: Do you understand the term 'confidence level'?

> *Example: The sample of 100 Sparklight bulbs had a mean life ($\bar{x}$) of 699.7 hr and a standard deviation (s) of 19.3 hr. What is the actual mean life of all Sparklight bulbs to the 99 per cent confidence level? (i.e. there is only a 1% risk that our result will be incorrect).*
>
> *Since n = 100, $\bar{x}$ = 699.7 and s = 19.3, we can say that the Standard Error (S.E.) is*
>
> *S.E. = $s/\sqrt{n}$ = 19.3/$\sqrt{100}$ = <u>1.93 hr.</u>*
>
> *Hence:*
>
> μ *= $\bar{x} \pm 2.58$ S.E. for 99 per cent confidence*
> *= 699.7 ± (2.58 × 1.93) hr*
> *= 699.7 ± 4.98 hr.*

★ ## See Questions B1–B3

Thus we are 99 per cent certain that the true mean lies between 694.72 hr and 704.68 hr.

Once we have the results from a trial sample, we can look at the problem in reverse. What size of sample is needed in order to give us particular limits of accuracy? This is more likely to be the problem faced by, say, an opinion research organisation wishing to assess voting intentions, or a market research department attempting to assess product awareness.

In the example just considered, we said that the true mean life (μ) of *all* Sparklight bulbs was given by:

699.7 $\pm$ 4.98 hr.

The figure of $\pm$ 4.98 hr is therefore the *level of accuracy* (L) of the observation. Look at how it was obtained:

$L = (2.58 \times 1.93)$ hr $= 4.98$ hr.

We multiplied the standard error of our sample observation (S.E.) by the z-value corresponding to the level of confidence required (z).

So: $L = $ (S.E.) $\times (z)$

But since S.E. $= s/\sqrt{n}$ (from Section 10.2.3) we can say that:

$L = s/\sqrt{n} \times z$

Hence $\quad \sqrt{n} = \dfrac{sz}{L}$

and so $n = \left(\dfrac{sz}{L}\right)^2$.

Hence we can find the n, the size of the sample required to give any specified level of accuracy (L), knowing only the sample standard deviation (s) and the z score for required confidence level (z).

$$n = \left(\frac{sz}{L}\right)^2$$

Example: We saw earlier that a sample of 100 Sparklight bulbs had a mean life
($\bar{x}$) of 699.7 hr and a standard deviation (s) of 19.3 hr.
What sample size must be taken to ensure:
a. A level of accuracy of $\pm$ 1 hr at the 99 per cent confidence level?
b. A level of accuracy of $\pm$ 1 hr at the 95 per cent confidence level?
In both cases:

S = 19.3 hr
L = 1.0 hr.

For 99 per cent confidence level, z = $\pm$ 2.58 (from tables)
For 95 per cent confidence level, z = $\pm$ 1.96 (from tables)

So:

a. $n = \left(\dfrac{19.3 \times 2.58}{1.0}\right)^2 = \underline{2479}$

b. $n = \left(\dfrac{19.3 \times 1.96}{1.0}\right)^2 = \underline{1431}$

So we can see what we know qualitatively: the larger the sample size, the greater the accuracy of our knowledge (in this case, an increased level of confidence in our result).

Pause for breath: Can you distinguish between level of confidence and level of accuracy?

10.4 Comparing Population and Sample Results

We frequently wish to determine whether a given sample result is consistent with a particular population, or whether it reflects a significant departure from the norm. An example might be taking samples of a machine's output to decide whether or not it is in need of adjustment because there has been a significant shift from the acceptable standard of output.

> *Example: Merrion's tests on a sample of Sparklight bulbs gave a mean life ($\bar{x}$) of 699.7 hr with a standard deviation (s) of 19.3 hr. The manufacturers claim that their bulbs have a mean life of 710 hr (μ). Is the Merrion result consistent with this figure?*

The test is one of statistical significance. Is the sample result *significantly* different from the population? In general, a significance test is carried out by assuming that there is *no* significant difference between observations unless the test proves to a given level of confidence that this is not the case. The level of confidence required depends on the implications of being wrong. Proving that there *is* a lack of awareness of our product needs a high level of confidence if we are to commit hundreds of thousands of pounds to a promotional campaign. Similarly, proving that a worker *is* less productive (and hence should be fired) is another situation demanding high confidence levels. Let us examine the stages in more detail.

10.4.1 State Null and Alternative Hypotheses

A null ('no difference') hypothesis is assumed to exist unless the test proves otherwise. In the example, the null hypothesis would be that there is *no* significant difference between the sample data and the manufacturer's claim. The alternative hypothesis says that there *is* a difference.

Pause for breath: What does the null hypothesis state, and when is it rejected?

10.4.2 Determine Hypothesis Rejection Area

This takes place in two stages:

a. Determine the confidence level required (usually 95%, 99% or 99.9%), which gives the desired level of certainty of our findings.

b. Determine the region in which the null hypothesis will be rejected. It is usual to assume that the null hypothesis will be rejected if there is a significant difference in either direction.

Figure 10.2 shows the case of 95 per cent confidence level (i.e. a 5 per cent chance of incorrect rejection of the null hypothesis).

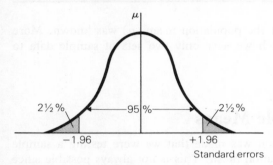

Fig. 10.2: Rejection areas for test to 95 per cent confidence

10.4.3 Determine Whether Deviation is Significant

This requires us to:

a. Determine the standard error of our sample observation (S.E.) which, for sample size $n \geq 30$ will be:

$$S.E. = s/\sqrt{n}$$

In the example, S.E. $= 19.3/\sqrt{100} = 1.93$ hr.

b. Determine the deviation of the sample and population means in terms of z standard errors:

$$z = \frac{\bar{x} - \mu}{S.E.}$$

For Sparklight bulb test:

$$z = \frac{699.7 - 710}{1.93} = \underline{-5.34 \text{ S.E.'s}}.$$

c. Compare observed deviation with that required for rejection. Any deviation greater than $z = \pm 1.96$ S.E.'s will take us into the null hypothesis rejection area. Here the result certainly is significant at the 95 per cent confidence level. Indeed, a z-value of -5.34 S.E.'s would allow us to reject the null hypothesis with even greater confidence! The table below gives appropriate values for rejection for various confidence levels (check the figures for yourselves using Appendix B).

	Confidence level (%)	Reject at this level if z-value exceeds: (S.E.'s)
Significant	95	± 1.96
Highly significant	99	± 2.58
Very highly significant	99.9	± 3.29

In this example, the value of the population mean (μ) was known. More likely is the situation in which we have only two sets of sample data to work with.

10.5 Comparing Sample Means

In the last section the assumption was made that we were testing a sample arithmetic mean against a population mean. This is not always possible since sometimes we have two samples. In this case we cannot assume that both samples come from that same population. We will be asking whether the difference between the means is merely due to natural variation as found in any sampling process or whether there is a significant difference between them. Suppose Sparklight and Morelight samples produced the data shown below:

	Sparklight	*Morelight*
Number in sample	100	200
Mean life of sample (hr)	699.7	694.3
Standard deviation (hr)	19.3	18.9

The process of significance testing is carried out in a similar manner to that in Section 10.4. The null hypothesis is that there is no difference between Sparklight and Morelight, whilst the alternative states that there *is*, with no implied direction of difference.

Let us suppose that we wish to work to a confidence level of 95 per cent or better.

In the case of two samples, the standard errors must be combined before the z-value can be calculated. The formula for the combined standard error is:

$$\text{S.E.} = \sqrt{\frac{s_1^2}{n_1} + \frac{s_2^2}{n_2}}$$

Where s_1 and s_2 are the standard deviations of samples 1 and 2 and n_1 and n_2 are the two sample sizes.

In the case of Morelight and Sparklight bulbs, this becomes:

$$\text{S.E.} = \sqrt{\frac{(19.3)^2}{100} + \frac{(18.9)^2}{200}}$$
$$= \sqrt{3.73 + 1.79} = \sqrt{5.52} = \underline{2.35.}$$

The deviation between the two sample means is $(x_1 - x_2)$ so the z-value of the deviation is:

★
$$z = \frac{x_1 - x_2}{\text{S.E.}}$$
$$= \frac{(699.7 - 694.3)}{2.35}$$
$$= \frac{5.4}{2.35}$$
$$= \underline{2.30.}$$

So we can conclude that the difference *is* significant at the 95 per cent confidence level (though *not* at the 99% level). Sparklight bulbs *do* last longer, (or else there is a serious sampling defect).

★ See Question B6 and B7

Work Section

A. Revision Questions

A1 What is the difference between a sample and a population?

A2 Write the symbols used for the mean and standard deviation of
   a. A population.
   b. A sample drawn from a population.

A3 What is the relationship between a population distribution and a distribution of the means of samples drawn from it?

A4 What (in words) is the standard error?

A5 How is the standard error related to the standard deviation (s) of a sample of n observations (where $n > 30$).

A6 What is the confidence level of a sample observation?

A7 Distinguish between level of confidence and level of accuracy.

A8 What is the general sequence of stages in a significance test?

A9 What is meant by the null hypothesis?

A10 Sketch the rejection areas for a 99 per cent confidence level in a significance test.

B. Exercises/Case Studies

B1 A sample of 50 students reveals that the mean time spent on revision for an exam is 62.5 hr, with a standard deviation of 15 hr.
   a. What is the standard error of the observation?
   b. What is the true mean time spent on revision to a confidence level of:
      i. 90 per cent; ii. 95 per cent; iii. 99 per cent?

B2 As part of a stock control programme, sample orders are studied to establish the company's delivery performance. 120 orders gave a mean delivery time of 30 days, with a standard deviation of 7 days. What answer would you give to a customer who wants to know the mean delivery delay likely (to a 95% confidence level)?
   How many orders would you need to study to give him an answer accurate to within one day at the quoted confidence level?

B3 A manufacturer wishes to estimate the mean dimension of a product and would be satisfied if it could be estimated to within ± 0.01 mm of the true mean with a 95 per cent level of confidence. An initial sample had a standard deviation of 0.20 mm. What sample size should be examined?

B4 A packing machine is designed to fill packs with a mean weight of 30.0 g. A sample of 75 packs showed a mean of 30.5 g with a standard deviation of 0.45 g. Is this evidence for the claim that the machine is not meeting its design specification?

B5 The head of an inner city school feels that his exam results are good given the school's low ability intake. The mean I.Q. of his most recent intake of 165 students was 96.4, with a standard deviation of 14.2. Do you support his view that the intake is below average?

B6 A sweet manufacturer has obtained the following figures on annual confectionery consumption:

	North	South
Sample size	845	1,440
Mean annual consumption (kg)	25	24
Standard deviation (kg)	6.5	6.0

Is there any evidence to suggest that the consumption pattern varies by area?

B7 The mean output/man/shift at a quarry is 4.9 tonnes (S.D. = 0.7 tonnes). That from another similar quarry is 4.7 tonnes (S.D. = 0.6 tonnes). In each case, the output was obtained from a sample study of 50 workers. Is there any evidence for the view that the first quarry is more productive than the second?

B8 Jenny James had recently been on a factory visit, and had seen operators using 'control charts'. These were used as part of a sampling procedure, in which an operator took regular samples of 30 items, and plotted the mean value on the chart. The chart looked like the one below:

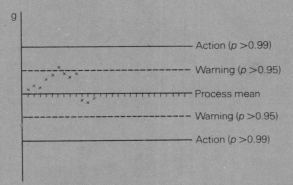

If the sample mean fell between the lines marked 'Warning' and 'Action', the operator was warned that the process was 'drifting' from its setting. Once a plot fell outside the 'Action' level, the process was stopped and reset.

a. Explain why such a chart can be used to monitor quality.
b. Explain how the position of the 'Action' and 'Warning' lines might be fixed relative to the mean line.
c. Jenny observed a large number of biscuits coming off a production line. The mean weight was 15 g with a standard deviation of 2 g. What value will the action and warning limits take if an operator is to plot the mean weight of samples of 30 biscuits at regular intervals?

C. Essay Questions

C1 Discuss how a knowledge of the concept of the standard error in sampling might be of benefit:
a. To a marketing manager; b. To a production manager; c. To a research scientist.
C2 A researcher has been asked to determine the degree of support for a particular political party. What statistical factors should be considered when designing a poll?
C3 Explain to a non-numerate (but intelligent) friend why (and how) the accuracy of sampling increases with the size of sample taken.

Part III Time in Decisions
Chapter 11

The Use of Index Numbers

Objectives: *To show how complex data can be represented as indices and to examine how such indices may be used.*

Plan of the chapter:

11.1 Case

The Statistics Department of Merrion County Council have been asked to present information on trends in relation to how the cost of living has been changing. This information is to be used in wage negotiations between the Council and its employees. Both sides in the negotiations are anxious to have 'appropriate' information and have agreed in principle that a measure of cost of living increases based on indices might provide such information. It becomes clear however that the actual figures derived in such indices can change according to the assumptions made with regard to the initial inputs to the indices.

11.2 Introduction

Anyone who regularly watches the television news or reads the financial pages of newspapers will be aware of the existence of indices. The newscaster wears a grave expression as the news is read: 'The latest **Retail Price Index** figures show inflation running at 10.2 per cent'.

On a more personal level indices increasingly dominate discussions with respect to wage and salary negotiations. One example of this is that decisions relating to such negotiations are often strongly influenced by changes in price levels as measured by such indices as the Retail Price Index. Further, these indices are sometimes used by companies in their determination of future prices. Thus, for example, when British Rail say that the 'real' price change for a service will be £x, what they really mean is that the price will go up by £x plus whatever further percentage is necessary to cover the Retail Price Index change for the period under consideration. Another example of where indices can affect us on a personal level is on government savings schemes where the 'interest' paid is directly determined by changes in the Retail Price Index – a feature that is incorporated in some of the Save As you Earn savings schemes.

In fact it would be difficult to think of an example where, as individuals, the quality of our lives were not affected in some way or other by decisions made on information completed and presented in the form of some index. In these circumstances it is important to understand the principles underlying index number construction. In more practical terms it is also important to understand what particular indices attempt to measure and to determine their effectiveness.

In this chapter we will highlight the basic questions that may be asked of any index so that one can change these into specific questions relating to a specific index under examination.

11.3 Simple Binary Index Numbers

In some types of problem, the underlying pattern is unclear because of the magnitude of the figures. We can say whether a quantity is increasing or decreasing with time, but by how much is less easy. It is more important to illustrate relative rather than absolute change.

Take, for example, Merrion's spending on education services. The pattern is shown below:

Year	19×0	19×1	19×2	19×3	19×4	19×5	19×6
Spending (£'000s)	11,430	12,590	13,280	15,410	18,300	22,360	23,100

We could relate expenditure in each year to that in a **base period**. Let us call the 19×0 value 100 expenditure units. Each year's value can now be related directly to this.

$$\text{Index for year } n = \frac{\text{Value for year } n}{\text{Value for base period}} \times 100$$

This is a *simple binary index* (consisting of two quantities).

So taking 19×0 as the base period, the 19×1 would have an index value of:

$$I_{19\times1} = \frac{12,590}{11,430} \times 100 = \underline{110.15}.$$

The full index series is shown in Fig. 11.1

Year	Expenditure (£'000s)	Index (19×0 = 100)
19×0	11,430	100
19×1	12,590	110.15
19×2	13,280	116.19
19×3	15,410	134.82
19×4	18,300	160.10
19×5	22,360	195.63
19×6	23,100	202.10

Fig. 11.1: Index of education expenditure

From Fig. 11.1 we can see that in 19×3, expenditure was nearly 35 per cent higher than in 19×0, whilst by 19×6, it had doubled.

What of *annual* percentage increases? Between 19×3 and 19×4, the index has risen by 25.28 index points, i.e. an increase of

$$\frac{25.28}{134.82} \times 100 = \underline{18.8} \text{ per cent over the year.}$$

A great advantage of index numbers is that they allow us to compare directly two or more factors measured in dissimilar units. So if Merrion was looking at road repair costs, it might wish to compare expenditure (£) with the number of vehicle registrations in the district.

If both sets of data are converted to index form, having a common base period, the relative movements can readily be seen, as shown below.

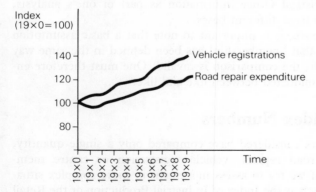

Fig. 11.2: Comparing indices

Turning the pages of journals such as *The Economist* will reveal such comparisons. Average earnings versus retail prices, wholesale prices versus industrial output or money supply versus retail prices are possible candidates for such comparison.

In the example above, the base periods of the two indices coincided but we may have two separate indices with different base periods. Suppose that we wished to compare recreation centre membership in Merrion with that in neighbouring Pendlebury; Merrion's figures started in 19×0 whilst those for Pendlebury started in 19×2.

| | *Recreation centre membership indices* | | | | | | | | |
	19×0	19×1	19×2	19×3	19×4	19×5	19×6	19×7	19×8	19×9
Merrion	100	104	109	114	119	125	131	137	140	143
Pendlebury			100	107	109	113	116	120	126	132

Fig. 11.3: Index series with different base periods

Direct comparison would be misleading, so we should adjust the base period of the Merrion series to coincide with that for Pendlebury (19×2).

All that is needed is to multiply each Merrion value by 100/109, giving the 'corrected' comparison below.

	19×0	19×1	19×2	19×3	19×4	19×5	19×6	19×7	19×8	19×9
Merrion	91.7	95.4	100	104.6	109.2	114.7	120.2	125.7	128.4	131.2
Pendlebury			100	107	109	113	116	120	126	132

Fig. 11.4: Index series corrected to same base period

The ability to adjust index series in this way may be particularly important when using Central Statistical Office information as part of one's analysis, since different series may have different bases.

In the simple index above, it is important to note that a basic assumption was made. It is assumed that 'membership' has been defined in the same way in both towns. If it is not, the comparison is invalid. One must therefore ensure that comparison is conducted between like and like.

11.4 Weighted Index Numbers

So far, the index numbers considered have compared only a single quantity, education expenditure, road repairs, vehicle registration or centre membership. What happens if we try to assess movement in more complex situations? National indices such as the Index of Industrial Production or the Retail Price Index are made up of many items. The latter is a measure of domestic spending on a wide range of goods and services, each showing price movements. How can they be combined to give an overall picture?

Example: The State of Simplistica has only two national products, telegraph poles and matches (both produced from its ample forest reserves). In 19×0, it produced 1 million tons of telegraph poles and 1 ton of matches. By 19×5, the outputs were 1.2 million tons and 5 tons respectively. The Ministry of Information wishes to produce an index of industrial production. We could treat each of the two factors as a separate binary index series and then combine the results.

	19×0		19×5	
	Tons	Index	Tons	Index
Telegraph poles	1 m.	100	1.2 m.	120
Matches	1	100	5	500

Hence one could say that the average *index of production in 19×5 was*

$$\frac{120 + 500}{2} = \underline{310} \ (19 \times 0 = 100)$$

This result implies that industrial production is three times greater in 19×5, yet it is clear that this is very misleading.

Simplistica's problems have arisen because matches and telegraph poles have been given equal importance. But it is clear that telegraph poles are *far* more important to the economy (and index) than matches, and this fact must be taken into account.

This can be done by weighting the various components of the index in order to give their relative importances.

Example: Simplistican households have only three items of expenditure, bread, fuel and matches. Prices of each are shown below, together with index values (19×0 = 100).

Item	19×0	19×5	19×5 Index (19×0 = 100)
Bread (*pence/loaf*)	18	22	122.2
Fuel (*pence/kWh*)	76	95	125.0
Matches (*pence/box*)	2.5	4	160.0

The relative importance of the three items might be assessed by a study of consumer expenditure. Suppose that fuel accounted for half of all spending, bread one third and matches one sixth. We could now modify our earlier indices by **weighting**.

Item	19×5 Index	Weighting	Weighted index
Bread	122.2	2	244.4
Fuel	125.0	3	375.0
Matches	160.0	1	160.0

Total weighted index = 779.4
Total weight = 6

$$weighted \ index = \frac{779.4}{6} = \underline{129.9} \ (19 \times 0 = 100)$$

Whilst the arithmetic of index construction is fairly straightforward, the construction of practical indices for general use needs rather more care, largely because they will run for long periods, and so errors may be compounded.

11.5 Practical Considerations

In producing indices for general use, statisticians must give careful thought to a number of areas if an index is to have lasting value. These include:

a. Determining which items to include in an index.

b. Determining the base period.

c. Determining the weights to be used.

Let us look at each in more detail.

11.5.1 Determining Items for Inclusion

This depends on the purpose of the index. Construction should bear in mind likely users and their needs, and the purpose should be clearly stated so that all users understand its relevance and limitations.

In producing an index with many components, such as an index of retail prices, the survey team must be selective. It would be impossible to include *all* possible items. Hence it is likely that the most important items will be identified from a sample survey. The composition of the sample will need to reflect the overall purpose of the index. A national index of retail prices will therefore look at a national sample stratified by socio-economic status, age, geographical location etc. An index of industrial production would use a sample based on different industries, sizes of firm, locations and ownership patterns.

With long-running indices, there are two particular problems. The first is that what is representative for the base year may not be representative for the current year. Often new products appear on the market that become quickly accepted as the normal requirement of life, such as a TV set. Very few families would have had one in 1955 and now most families have TV sets. Another example would clearly be in the electronic field as a result of the micro chip revolution.

The second is, what may seem to be the same item may be enormously different in terms of quality – e.g. wireless sets to transistors. On face value one might assume that one was comparing like with like, but, of course, this would not be the case. Periodic up-dating of long-life indices is therefore necessary.

11.5.2 Determining the Base Period

The base period must be chosen with care, as it must be a 'typical' period. Thus a retail price index for the UK with a base in 1940 would not satisfy this requirement. Similarly a share price index with a base period in the middle of a steep economic recession would be of dubious merit.

11.5.3 Determining the Weights to be Used

In Section 11.4 we did not consider how the weights were determined. As with other areas of index construction, they are likely to be based on sample survey work. Thus the commodities in a prices index may be weighted by the percentage of expenditure they account for in the 'average household'. In a company, an earnings index may need to be weighted by the number of employees in each pay grade.

Although in practice one would attempt to take into account the relative importance of items by objective assessments, this is not always possible where 'services' are involved.

It is even more difficult to determine weights when comparisons are taken over long periods of time since, of course, the quantities used of a commodity varies as purchasing habits change. If the quantities of commodities are different for different periods then so will the weights appropriate to them. Not only may the weights be radically different when undertaking comparisons over long periods of time, but so too may the prices attached to the commodities. Both of these make comparisons difficult.

In an attempt to overcome these difficulties two different approaches have been developed.

The Laspeyre Index uses weights determined for the base period throughout. It takes the form

$$I_L = \frac{\Sigma a_n b_0}{\Sigma a_0 b_0}$$

where:
- a = Index factor
- b = Weight factor
- 0 = Base period
- n = Current period

The Paasche Index uses a constantly updated weighting factor for each item, and takes the form

$$I_P = \frac{\Sigma a_n b_n}{\Sigma a_0 b_n} \,.$$

The Paasche index is therefore more applicable to situations where the relative weights of factors change frequently. This increased relevance is paid for by the need to collect weight data for each period of the index – often a time consuming and expensive operation. (A Laspeyre Index, periodically updated, may sometimes be used as a compromise).

Example: A prices index is to be constructed, and information on both prices and relative quantities has been obtained for two years.

Commodity	Unit	Prices (p) Base year (a_0)	Current year (a_n)	Quantities Base year (b_0)	Current year (b_n)
Bread	1 loaf	10	24	100	90
Tea	1 lb	24	27	10	8
Potatoes	7 lb	18	24	20	30
Milk	1 qt	7	12	7	10

Note that the index is one of prices *weighted by* quantities (*and so a and b refer to price and quantity respectively*).

From the formulae above, the two indices for the current year are:

$$I_L = \frac{\Sigma a_n b_0}{\Sigma a_0 b_0} = \frac{(24 \times 100) + (27 \times 10) + (24 \times 20) + (12 \times 7)}{(10 \times 100) + (24 \times 10) + (18 \times 20) + (7 \times 7)}$$

$$= \frac{3,234}{1,649} = 1.96$$

i.e. <u>196</u> (*since base period* = 100)

$$I_P = \frac{\Sigma a_n b_n}{\Sigma a_0 b_n} = \frac{(24 \times 90) + (27 \times 8) + (24 \times 30) + (12 \times 10)}{(10 \times 90) + (24 \times 8) + (18 \times 30) + (7 \times 10)}$$

$$= \frac{3,216}{1,702} = 1.89$$

i.e. <u>189</u> (*base period* = 100).

Had we produced a quantities *index weighted by* price (*taking values a and b respectively*), *rather different figures would result for the current year*:

$$I_L = 109.9, \qquad I_P = 99.4 \ (base \ period = 100).$$

(*We can therefore see that expenditure changes have occurred largely as a result of price change rather than quantity changes.*)

There seems to be no way of distinguishing, on theoretical grounds, the advantages of the Paasche and Laspeyre indices. Yet they give different numerical answers in relation to the same data and therefore they both 'interpret' the data slightly differently.

At one time this was deemed to be a disadvantage and statisticians attempted to develop other theoretical indices that overcame the so-called difficulties associated with Paasche and Laspeyre.

11.5.4 The Retail Price Index

One government index that we should note in particular is the Index of Retail Prices constructed monthly and published in the Department of Employment Gazette. This is not only used to measure inflationary trends but, as we have noted, is also used in 'bargaining' for changes of wages and salaries. This index originated in 1953 with the Household Expenditure Survey conducted by the then Ministry of Labour. In this survey, each person in 20,000 selected households was asked to keep a detailed record of what was spent over a three-week period. In fact only 11,600 household budgets were used to determine the 'weights' given by the public to various items. The weights were determined by the percentage of income spent on individual commodities. Thus with an aggregate weight of 1,000, the weight for food was 350 indicating that a representative consumer could spend 35.0 per cent of his income on food.

As purchasing habits have changed so have weights given to individual commodities. The weights are now based on a Family Expenditure Survey covering a sample of 5,000 households each year. No one year's figures are used in isolation since some items, such as cookers, are bought infrequently which could cause large irregularities in the figures. To overcome this the weights are determined by the average of the previous three year's expenditure patterns disclosed by the survey.

It is important to remember that the RPI covers the hypothetical 'Joe and Josephine Average' who live in Meantown, Midshire. Non-smoking families who grow their own vegetables and walk to work/school will be affected rather differently to the Average family!

11.6 Conclusion

It now seems to be accepted that no index is or can be 'perfect' and each will have some difficulties associated with it. Which one is the most appropriate to use depends therefore on broader issues than technical considerations based on theoretical tests. These broader issues will include the availability of representative data if statisticians are to calculate their own indices. More often than not however, government indices are used as important inputs in managerial decision-making situations. In these cases the broader issues will be with respect to the statistical soundness of the index particularly as to the choice of base year and what is to be measured. Above all however the choice of which to use will largely be determined by its appropriateness and acceptability to the parties concerned. Each party – say in wage negotiations – will naturally wish to choose that index that will further the line of argument that it wishes to pursue. We have noted in this chapter that there are many indices to choose from. It is important to recognise not only what they attempt to do but also that different indices may give different numerical results even when they purport to do the same things in principle. It is interesting to compare the values of the Retail Prices Index with those of the Tax and Prices Index. The latter was introduced in 1979 to produce a 'fairer' picture of the effect of price and tax changes. By 1982, the two indices were showing rather different results.

In relation to the particular problems stated in the case at the beginning of the chapter it ought to be clear therefore that there is no definitive answer with respect to which index ought to be used. The answer is that it 'all depends on what you are attempting to show'.

Work Section

A. Revision Questions

A1 What is the base period of an index?

A2 Give three examples of nationally published indices and explain what they show.

A3 Show how two or more indices can be used to provide comparisons between unlike quantities.

A4 How can indices with different base periods be combined?

A5 Why do some indices need to contain 'weighting'?

A6 Give two different examples of weighted index, with examples of when they might be employed.

A7 How would one determine what factors to include in an index?

A8 How can weight factors be determined?

A9 Why might different parties at a negotiation prefer to base their views on different indices?

A10 Why should the Retail Price Index be treated with caution?

B. Exercises/Case Studies

B1 Determine how each of the following indices is constructed, taking note of the weighting methods employed:
    a. The Retail Price Index.
    b. The FT Ordinary Share Index.
    c. The Index of Industrial Production.

B2 As a cost analyst with a petroleum company, you are asked to compile an annual index for the cost of drilling an oil well for each year since 19×0, with 19×1 as the base period. In 19×1 the cost of drilling was made up of 60 per cent labour and 40 per cent materials, and you accept that the following data adequately represents these cost elements.

Year	Average hourly Earnings (£s)	Price index for materials
19×0	2.41	98.8
19×1	2.58	100.0
19×2	2.75	102.6
19×3	3.00	108.5
19×4	3.28	116.7
19×5	3.58	119.0

   a. Calculate an earning index (19×1 = 100).
   b. Calculate a total drilling cost index for each year.
   c. What is the percentage increase in drilling costs between 19×0 and
      19×5?

(Cambridge Local Examinations Syndicate A Level)

B3 Calculate an unweighted price index for the following items:

Item	Year I	Year II
Tobacco (pence per ounce)	25	53
Beer (pence per pint)	12	34
Petrol (pence per gallon)	35	112
Rates (pence per day)	10	32

B4 Using the following weights calculate the weighted price index and compare the results with those of B3:

Item	Weights in year I
Tobacco	4
Beer	5
Petrol	6
Rates	3

B5 The following information has been extracted from a company's payroll records:

	Unskilled workers		Semi-skilled workers		Skilled workers	
	Average weekly wages	Average number employed	Average weekly wages	Average number employed	Average weekly wages	Average number employed
19×5	42.10	156	45.50	112	50.30	84
19×7	48.70	207	49.90	125	52.60	78

Calculate an index number for all weekly wages for 19×7 using 19×5 as a base year and the average numbers employed in 19×5 as the basis for the relative weights.

B6 For the data of B5 calculate an index number for all average weekly wages for 19×5 using 19×7 as a base year and the average numbers employed in 19×7 as the base for relative weights.

B7 From the following data calculate the Laspeyre Index for each of the periods:

Commodity	Base period		Period I		Period II	
	Price (£)	Quantity	Price (£)	Quantity	Price (£)	Quantity
A	36	100	40	95	42	90
B	80	12	90	10	100	10
C	45	16	41	18	41	20
D	15	115	16	120	18	120
E	5	1,100	6	1,200	6	1,400
F	150	70	150	60	180	60

B8 For the data in B7 calculate the Paasche Index and compare the results with those of B7.

B9 Calculate the Paasche and Laspeyre indices for each of the periods for the following data:

Commodity	Base period		Period I		Period II	
	Price (£)	Quantity	Price (£)	Quantity	Price (£)	Quantity
1	6	50	7	60	8	65
2	5	30	6	35	9	30
3	4	90	3	85	4	80
4	10	40	11	35	10	40
5	9	10	8	10	10	10

Comment on your results.

B10 A company employs three grades of male direct operators, M1, M2 and M3 and three grades of female direct operators, F1, F2 and F3. The following represents numbers of operators employed and rates paid over three years:

Labour grade	19×5		19×6		19×7	
	Rate p/h (£)	No. of operators	Rate p/h (£)	No. of operators	Rate p/h (£)	No. of operators
M1	0.66	32	0.73	33	0.80	35
M2	0.62	14	0.68	12	0.74	10
M3	0.56	16	0.60	14	0.66	12
F1	0.44	40	0.52	42	0.64	45
F2	0.41	18	0.47	18	0.58	16
F3	0.36	25	0.42	26	0.52	30

a. Adopting 19×5 as the base, calculate an index number for the average wage for 19×6 and 19×7 using:
   i base weighting formula; and
   ii current weighting formula.
b. State, with reasons, which method you would employ in a business situation.

C. Essay Questions

C1 What considerations must be borne in mind when an index number is compiled? You should illustrate your answer by reference to an index number with which you are familiar.

C2 A company has reached an agreement with representatives of its employees that wages and salaries will in future be tied to a local cost of living index which the company will compile. Advise the company how they should gather information and compile this local cost of living index. What are the problems the company will encounter in completing this exercise?

C3 Discuss the relative advantages and disadvantages of using base year and current year weights. Are there any alternatives to the two methods?

Chapter 12

Forecasting Methods

Objectives: *To show how decision makers can make future predictions based on careful evaluation of past data and events.*

Plan of the chapter:

- **12**.1 Case
- **12**.2 Introduction
- **12**.3 Qualitative Forecasting
  - **12**.3.1 The Delphi Technique
  - **12**.3.2 Panel Consensus
- **12**.4 Time Series Analysis
  - **12**.4.1 Extracting the Trend
  - **12**.4.2 Identifying the Seasonal Variation
  - **12**.4.3 Random Variations
- **12**.5 Extrapolation Methods
- **12**.6 The Use of Forecasts

12.1 Case

Merrion Education Committee are concerned about the number of teachers that it will need to recruit in the future to satisfy the educational objectives set by the County.

In particular the Committee is concerned for the years after 1985 in relation to Primary Schools for children from 5 to under 8 years old, and for Middle Schools for children between 8 and 12 years old. The Committee has agreed that the average pupil/teacher ratio for these groups should be 25 and 20 respectively.

The Committee has asked the Statistics Department to collect data in relation to potential problems and, on the basis of analysis, to provide the Committee with a prediction of the number of teachers required after 1980.

12.2 Introduction

The statistical techniques so far examined help deal with present problems based on existing data. These day-to-day problems comprise a substantial part of the challenge of management. They are often deemed routine, repetitive 'tactical' problems.

There is another set of problems that arises from the challenge of the future. In broad terms, two questions are generally asked. The first refers to predicting what might happen in the future and the second is concerned with making decisions *now* based on these predictions. In Merrion's case the prediction part will be how many 5 to 8 year olds will need educating in the Council's area from five years hence. The second type of consideration will entail deciding on such things as building programmes, land purchase or sales, the purchase of equipment etc. as well as ensuring the correct supply of teachers. It must be emphasised therefore that forecasting involves not only predicting what might happen, but also making decisions to ensure that, in the light of **forecasts**, objectives can be met.

It is probable that the variable most likely to affect the demand for teachers will be the number of children in Merrion Council's area. Given the age groups under consideration and given that the first prediction is for 1985, the children would have to be born in or before 1980. Suppose the figures are those shown below:

School year	1973	1974	1975	1976	1977	1978	1979	1980
Numbers	4,160	4,430	4,450	4,250	4,170	3,930	3,840	3,760

From this we could deduce, as a first approximation, the number of children in the First and Middle Schools in 1985. For the First School the 5 to under 8's will comprise of those children born in 1978, 1979, and 1980, a total of 11,530 children. For the Middle School, the children will be those born in the years 1973–1977, a total of 21,460.

Thus a first approximation of the number of teachers required (assuming the pupil/teacher ratio of 25 in the Primary School and 20 in the Middle Schools) would be:

$$\text{First School} = \frac{11,530}{\text{pupil/teacher ratio}} = \frac{11,530}{25} = 461$$

$$\text{Middle school} = \frac{21,160}{\text{pupil/teacher ratio}} = \frac{21,160}{20} = 1,058$$

But the number of births in the Merrion catchment area is only part of the story. Some families will move away whilst others will arrive. Since Merrion is keen to attract new industries, there could well be a net gain in the number of small children in the area. The school population will therefore be bound up with the general economic health of the area.

Faced with such problems, Merrion's decision makers have two broad avenues of exploration. Firstly, they can use qualitative forecasting techniques where data are scarce. Alternatively, they can employ quantitative methods where figures *are* available.

The approach here is fairly typical of what happens in forecasting situations. Most people take the view that what has happened in the past is likely to be repeated in the future. The sun rose yesterday and will rise again tomorrow. In fact, many forecasts of the future are extrapolations of what has happened in the past, on the assumption that nature does repeat itself. For example, actuaries assume life patterns, economists have assumed trade cycles, and we try to 'learn lessons from history'. Let us now look at some approaches open to Merrion.

12.3 Qualitative Forecasting

There is no hard data available in relation to many questions, as there was with the population figures, since they are events that may or may not happen in the future. The forecaster has to use qualitative assessments which may later be quantified. The objective is to bring together all information and judgements which relate to the factors being estimated in a logical, unbiased and systematic way. This is particularly vital in areas of new technology with Research and Development in new products, or where people's attitudes and behaviour are expected to alter. In Merrion, the likely pattern of future industrial and commercial development falls into this category of problem. Two possible methods are the **'Delphi' technique** and that of **panel consensus**.

12.3.1 The Delphi Technique
In this a panel of experts is interrogated through a sequence of questionnaires. Each sequence of questionnaire construction, individual completion and analyses, builds on the answers of any previous questionnaires. Each expert is allowed to see the results of the analysis of the previous questionnaire but the panel never meet together. This latter is quite deliberate so that each expert will give a personal, considered opinion rather than be swayed by others in a group.

In Merrion's case the panel might include an economist from the local university, the head of the Council's development office, a financial analyst from the City. All have an informed opinion on trends in industrial and commercial development in the area. In addition, representatives from the education world will also have a place in the team.

12.3.2 Panel Consensus
Here, it is assumed that several experts working co-operatively can come to a better forecast than individuals in isolation. There is no secrecy, and the interplay of ideas is encouraged. This is because one person's idea, whilst being of little value in itself, can trigger a new and more fruitful line of thought in another. Both 'Delphi' and panel consensus have their strong points, and it is likely that both might be employed: 'Delphi' as a first stage and then panel consensus as a second.

Merrion carried out research and as a consequence of conducting the various analyses, the Statistics Department was unable to detect any signs of net migration for the forseeable future. However, they were still uneasy about accepting 461 and 1058 as the teacher estimates. Their main concern was that after 1977 birth rates seemed to be falling, and this might be a trend that was likely to continue. How could they determine the trend? The approach of Time Series Analysis is a useful tool here.

12.4 Time Series Analysis

Data gathering for past periods can be analysed to see what might have affected the results. A careful analysis will allow the figures to be broken down into three components:

a. ·A **trend**: which is the underlying movement of the time series. On balance, are the values tending to rise, fall or remain static?

b. **Seasonal** or **cyclical variations**: Superimposed on the trend will be regular variations. On a daily basis, public transport utilisation shows two regular peaks, whilst annually, ice cream sales peak in the summer. The economy as a whole goes through a series of 'ups and downs' over several years.

c. **Random variations**: In addition to the regular movements of trend and seasonal factors, there will be 'out of the blue' events which affect data. The Middle East oil embargo in 1973 had wide-reaching effects, as would a national transport strike. In Merrion's case, the effects of winter electricity cuts on the pattern of births would be such a variation.

In order to separate the three components above from data, one of the simplest techniques is that of **moving averages**.

Example: The sales of a firm vary over time as shown in Fig. 12.1 below.

Sales revenue (£'000s)

Year	Quarters			
	1	*2*	*3*	*4*
1	*120*	*112*	*102*	*120*
2	*122*	*118*	*110*	*131*
3	*130*	*127*	*115*	

Fig. 12.1: Sales variation over time

Presented graphically, Fig. 12.2, we can make certain qualitative observations.

A qualitative examination shows that the *general* trend is one of rising sales. Superimposed on this is an annual cycle (minimum sales in quarter 3, maximum in quarters 4 or 1). Let us now investigate the figures quantitatively, starting with the trend.

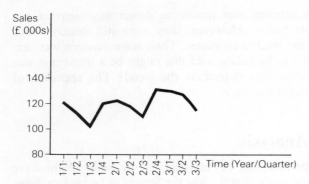

Fig. 12.2: Plot of sales vs. time

12.4.1 Extracting the Trend

The trend is the underlying movement of the data. Thus we must smooth out fluctuations. A useful device is to take averages. Hence for the three years in question, we could obtain:

Year 1: $\dfrac{120 + 112 + 102 + 120}{4} = 113.5$

Year 2: $\dfrac{122 + 118 + 110 + 131}{4} = 117.75$

Year 3: $\dfrac{130 + 127 + 115}{3} = 124.$

This certainly shows a rising trend, but gives only three points. Better is the idea of moving averages. This uses the fact that a year is any consecutive four quarters, and not merely a calendar year.

Thus after calculating an average of Year 1, Quarters 1 to 4, we can drop the first quarter's sales value and replace it with that for the Quarter 1, Year 2. The average has therefore 'moved' one quarter forward. We keep going until we end with an average of Year 2, Quarter 4, plus Year 3, Quarters 1 to 3. This is shown in Fig. 12.3 below.

Periods used (Yr/Qtr)	Moving average	= Trend
1/1, 1/2, 1/3, 1/4	(120+112+102+120) ÷ 4	= 113.5
1/2, 1/3, 1/4, 2/1	(112+102+120+122) ÷ 4	= 114.0
1/3, 1/4, 2/1, 2/2	(102+120+122+118) ÷ 4	= 115.5
1/4, 2/1, 2/2, 2/3	(120+122+118+110) ÷ 4	= 117.5
2/1, 2/2, 2/3, 2/4	(122+118+110+131) ÷ 4	= 120.25
2/2, 2/3, 2/4, 3/1	(118+110+131+130) ÷ 4	= 122.25
2/3, 2/4, 3/1, 3/2	(110+131+130+127) ÷.4	= 124.5
2/4, 3/1, 3/2, 3/3	(131+130+127+115) ÷ 4	= 125.75

Fig. 12.3: Calculating four–quarterly moving averages

One slight problem with the trend figures as calculated in Fig. 12.3 is that they do not fall on a particular quarter but between quarters. Since you would want to draw comparisons between the expected trend figure and the actual observation for the quarter, it is advisable to get trend figures that fall on a particular quarter. Thus the average for Year 1, Quarters 1 to 4 falls opposite Quarter 2½! Figure 12.4 shows this.

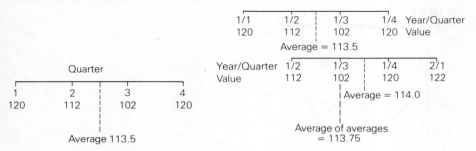

Fig. 12.4: Mean of four –quarter average

Fig. 12.5: 'Centreing' of two successive moving averages

We can achieve this by adding and averaging pairs of trend values obtained in Fig. 12.3. The resulting average is thus based on *eight* quarters' data. Figure 12.5 shows this process, known as **centreing**.

Note how the resulting average corresponds exactly with an actual value, that for Year 1, Quarter 3. In practice, it is easier to add the two successive 4-period moving totals together and divide the resulting total by 8. The full calculation is shown as a table in Fig. 12.6.

Yr/Qtr	Sales (£'000s)	4-Period moving total	8-Period moving total	Moving average trend
(a)	(b)	(c)	(d)	(e) = (d) ÷ 8
1/1	120			
1/2	112			
1/3	102			113.75
1/4	120	454		114.75
2/1	122	456	910	116.5
2/2	118	462	918	118.875
2/3	110	470	932	121.25
2/4	131	481	951	123.375
3/1	130	489	970	125.125
3/2	127	498	987	
3/3	115	503	1001	

Fig. 12.6: Sales and trend calculation for quarters

Note how the trend values are set against the appropriate quarter. (Look back at Fig. 12.5.)

A six- or eight-quarter moving average would give greater smoothing, but fewer points for comparison between trend and actual values. Conversely, a two-quarter moving average gives little smoothing. As in so many cases, one has to compromise.

Figure 12.7 below now shows the relationship between the original data and the trend.

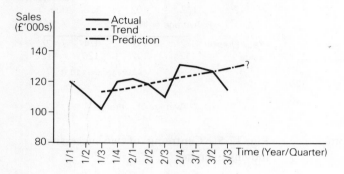

Fig. 12.7: Original and trend values compared

The trend line (whether straight or curved) can be extended to forecast the future trend line on the assumption that the trend of conditions previously measured will continue into the future (as shown by a broken line). Needless to say the further it is extended the more likely it will prove to be inaccurate as this simple assumption may not hold.

12.4.2 Identifying the Seasonal Variation
Looking at the original data, we can see that there is a seasonal pattern in the figures in addition to the upward trend. For example, in Fig. 12.7 we can see that two of the quarterly figures seem to be above the trend and two below. The 4th and 1st quarters' figures appear to be above the trend and the 2nd and 3rd below. This seems to be a consistent pattern in the figures we have. If we can calculate the *average* variation from the trend for each quarter this will enable us to forecast the quarterly figures around the extended trend by making adjustments. (It could also allow us to compare the performance of past quarters with one another, so the technique is important for reviewing past performance). To calculate these seasonal adjustments we compare the relevant trend figures, already found, with each actual sales figure.

Quarters	Sales (£'000s)	Moving average trend (£'000s)	Sales – trend = seasonal variation (£'000s)
1	120		
2	112		
3	102	113.75	−11.75
4	120	114.75	+ 5.25
1	122	116.5	+ 5.5
2	118	118.875	− 0.875
3	110	121.25	−11.25
4	131	123.375	+ 7.625
1	130	125.125	+ 4.875
2	127		
3	115		
4			

Fig. 12.8: Sales figures and seasonal patterns

The figures in the last column confirm that quarters 1 and 4 are above the trend and quarters 2 and 3 below. We could in fact calculate the average seasonal variation to use in our predictions, although from only one or two observations for each quarter this could not be expected to be very accurate.

The average seasonal variation for 1st quarter figures is therefore

$\{(+5.5) + (4.875)\} \div 2$, or $+ 5.1875$.

Overall, we obtain the following average seasonal variations for the four quarters.

Quarter	Average seasonal variation
1	+ 5.1875
2	− 0.875 (taking only one result)
3	−11.50
4	+ 6.4375

These average quarterly variations can now be used in addition to the extrapolated trend. The negative signs imply that we need to take the figures away from the trend figure for quarters 2 and 3. The average seasonal variations for quarters 1 and 4 should be added to the trend figure. Hence, if a projected trend value of £130,000 were to be obtained for the first quarter of Year 4, it would require upward revision by some £5,000.

12.4.3 Random Variations

As we said earlier, there is almost always some variation which is left unexplained. For example, if we wanted to predict the sales figure for the second quarter of Year 3 the prediction would be:

Prediction = Trend Figure + Average Seasonal Variation for the 2nd quarter =

127.25 (from graph) + (−0.875) = 126.375.

But, of course, we know from our original data that the *actual* sales are 127.
The random variation or unexplained variation is therefore:

127 − 126.375 = 0.625.

This is very small in comparison with the actual sales data and therefore we can infer that our forecasting procedure is a good one.

12.5 Extrapolation Methods

So far, we have been concerned with analysing the underlying pattern of past data. The ultimate purpose was to use this analysis as a means of making forecasts of future events. Clearly, no analysis will give a perfect prediction since the future is uncertain. But it can make managers more aware of the factors likely to need consideration.

In a case such as that in Fig. 12.9 below, a straight line trend might be extrapolated to a future period, the appropriate seasonal factor applied, and a first estimate produced.

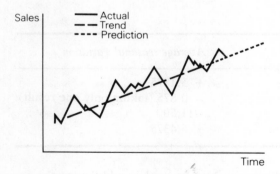

Fig. 12.9: Straight line extrapolation

We could refine the projection somewhat by quoting a *range* of values likely, since we have seen that random variations can be estimated, and hence allowed for. But what of the situation whose trend is shown in Fig. 12.10?

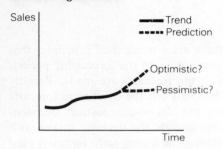

Fig. 12.10: Extrapolating a varying trend

A number of scenarios might be envisaged. The recent upward swing in the trend may be the start of an extended upward movement. But it may be short-lived, and the sales trend will level out or even fall. Perhaps the true answer lies between the two? Yet on the future estimate of sales might depend the future of a large capital investment programme.

Managers are most unlikely to base their decisions on a single analysis of past sales. They are likely to look at trends in a number of related time series. Thus someone making bicycles might look at trends in personal expenditure, fuel costs, public transport utilisation costs and so on, since these are factors which might play a part in future sales patterns. Consideration of forecasts for the economy as a whole (whether published by the Treasury, the CBI, or independent groups such as the St. James's Group or ITEM) would also be required. Such analysis would reveal the presence of a cycle of economic activity over and above the short term variation of sales through the year.

So far, we have assumed that all data carries equal weight. **Exponential smoothing** assigns different weights to historical and recent data in order to give the recent figures more emphasis in the analysis. Thus a warehouse ordering programme might 'load' the last six months figures in a twelve-month moving average at the expense of older results.

Lastly, it is as well to bear in mind a number of points when choosing the number of observations you will use in a moving average:
a. Where the data has a regular pattern of seasonality, a moving average with the same number of periods as the seasonality will give the greatest smoothing (e.g. 4 quarters, or 12 months).
b. An odd number of periods avoids the process of centreing (shown in Figs. 12.3 and 12.4).
c. The larger the number of observations taken on the moving average, the fewer points there will be on the trend line. (If you choose them all you will only have one.)
d. With a large number, the actual (rather than extrapolated) trend stops well short of the latest data.
e. If a large number is used, any new direction in the trend will take time to show itself and be identified as such. (Yet an average which is *too* sensitive may mislead in the opposite direction!)

12.6. The Use of Forecasts

Whatever forecasting methods are used there are a number of principles that have to be considered. One of the main ones relates to the forecasting period, that is the length of time ahead for which the forecasts are made. Broadly speaking, organisations use varying time horizons but the short-term forecasts are the most important when discussing the day-to-day tactical decision-making issues. These are the forecasts that provide the decision maker with the information needed for pressing decisions. The longer term forecasts tend to be concerned with 'scenario setting', that is drawing up 'broad brush' pictures of what might materialise in the more distant future. In response to these forecasts the manager must decide whether he agrees with what the forecasts suggest and, if he does, he must then decide what decisions and actions should be taken to ensure a part in that future. Agreement is normally a formality in the short term where there are stable conditions. In the longer term the number and importance of new factors, e.g. the price of oil, productivity of the economy, tax levels, major technology innovations or even war may make one forecast impossible. The alternative may be to give several, each with a probability of it occurring. Decisions may then be made with, at least, a greater awareness of the risks and possibly with planned future actions in the case of some of the worst contingencies arising. Shell Transport and Trading Company have recently found the future, 15 years ahead, so hard to forecast that they have given up traditional forecasts and simply paint two different scenarios of world development in the fields of society, politics, economies and technology: thus they are showing alternatives that could happen but making no attempt to say what will.

In the case of Merrion, their forecast could be based on information about students that was both cheap to gain from secondary sources and likely to be fairly accurate. As a result, they might use this forecast to produce plans for teacher recruitment, buildings, equipment etc. In the case of the sales example, simple short-term forecasting is useful although adjustments will need to be made for factors like consumer demand, competitors' actions, advances in technology.

Finally, as with all the statistical analyses, the question has to be asked whether the time expended and the cost incurred in the analysis is worth the benefit gained. Would an intelligent guess be as cost effective?

Work Section

A. Revision Questions

A1 What is a forecast?

A2 Distinguish between qualitative and quantitative forecasting techniques.

A3 How does the Delphi technique of forecasting differ from the panel consensus?

A4 What are the main steps in analysing a time series?

A5 What is a trend?

A6 Give three examples of short-term variations.

A7 Give three examples of cyclical variations.

A8 Explain the term 'random variations'.

A9 What does the phrase 'moving average' mean?

A10 Why is 'centreing' sometimes used when calculating short-term variations?

A11 Explain what 'exponential smoothing' is and why it is used.

A12 What assumptions do we make when using past events to forecast the future?

B. Exercises/Case Studies

B1 The supplies of bottled gas in the UK (million bottles) for the years $19 \times 0 - \times 3$ were as shown below:

| Year | Quarters | | | |
	1	2	3	4
19×0	23	14	10	16
19×1	23	15	12	22
19×2	28	20	16	28
19×3	33	23	17	

Plot a graph of the data.

B2   Plot a graph for the following figures:

Consumers' Expenditure on Wallpaper (£m.)

Year	Quarters			
	1	*2*	*3*	*4*
19×4	104	119	119	144
19×5	111	127	124	148
19×6	115	128	121	

B3   By means of an appropriate moving average find the trend for the data in B1 and draw the trend on your graph.

B4   By means of an appropriate moving average find the trend for the data in B2 and draw the trend on your graph.

B5   Calculate the average seasonal variation for the data in B1 and B3 and forecast the supply of gas for the fourth quarter of 19×3.

B6   Calculate the average seasonal variation for the data in B2 and B4 and forecast consumers expenditure on wallpaper for the 4th quarter of 19×6. Comment on your result.

B7   The following data give the index numbers for Industrial Production for the years 19×0–19×3. a. By calculating the appropriate moving average obtain the trend and seasonal factors for each quarter; b. forecast the index number for 19×4, quarter 1.

Year	Quarters			
	1	*2*	*3*	*4*
19×0				103.5
19×1	102.2	101.2	95.1	103.5
19×2	99.1	103.8	96.8	109.0
19×3	112.1	110.5	105.2	

B8   Sales of chemicals from a wholesale supplier showed the following monthly pattern

| Month | (Thousand bags) | |
	19×0	19×1
Jan.	105	113
Feb.	117	126
Mar.	130	139
Apl.	129	132
May	115	120
Jun.	113	116
Jul.	109	112
Aug.	122	128
Sep.	129	135
Oct.	136	141
Nov.	118	126
Dec.	112	122

a. Explain how the 6-monthly cycle might occur.
b. Produce a trend from the data using i. a   6-monthly   moving average
        ii. a   12-monthly   moving average.
c. Comment on your results.

B9   P.B. Cockle had been in the garage business in Utopia for some ten years. During this time he had seen many changes introduced into the trade in an attempt to broaden garages' operating bases, varying from the obvious, like servicing facilities to car washes, auto-shops and even cafeterias. Interesting and useful though these innovations were for limited periods of time, it had become obvious to him that 70 per cent of his trade was really concerned with the sale of petrol (motor spirit).

Unable to add any new ventures to his existing garages, and bearing in mind that 70 per cent of his trade was in petrol sales, he decided to concentrate his efforts on selling more petrol.

With prices steadily increasing, due to government taxation, it was clear to him that he would have to work hard to increase his volume of sales. His instinct suggested to him that a 5 per cent increase in sales volume in the next trading period would not be unrealistic. To achieve this, he was conscious that he would have to take on some promotion. He was prepared to consider using trading stamps and to join in a promotional scheme with a glass manufacturer; in addition to this, considerable local advertising would be necessary. All this would be expensive to implement and difficult to evaluate afterwards. Before committing himself to such expenditure, he decided to attempt a market analysis from the data he had available locally. He hoped this would throw some light on his proposed sales objective and promotional scheme.

Study the attached data carefully and then answer the following questions:

i. Show the trend in P.B. Cockle's sales during 1977–81.

ii. Petrol sales drop between the last quarter of one year and the first quarter of the next. How do you account for this and what significance might it have in relation to Mr. Cockle's planning?

iii. Using the range of data given, suggest a sales figure for the first quarter of 1982. Was Mr. Cockle's sales objective realistic?

iv. What would you advise him to do about his promotional plans? (Explain your reasons.)

Table 1   *P.B. Cockle: Sales of Motor Spirit 1977–81 (thousand tons)*

Year Quarter	1977	1978	1979	1980	1981
1	244	263	263	282	301
2	285	292	318	326	345
3	384	318	320	348	368
4	260	282	296	319	338

Source: Sales Statistics of Company

Table 2   *Utopian National Vehicle Data 1971–81*

	New registrations (m.)			No. of cars in use (m.)
	Cars	M/Cycles	All Vehicles	
1971	0.75	0.23	1.28	6.11
1972	0.80	0.15	1.22	6.71
1973	1.03	0.18	1.50	7.55
1974	1.22	0.22	1.75	8.44
1975	1.15	0.16	1.64	9.13
1976	1.09	0.12	1.53	9.75
1977	1.14	0.15	1.61	10.55
1978	1.14	0.12	1.60	11.08
1979	1.01	0.10	1.44	11.50
1980	1.13	0.12	1.56	11.80
1981	1.33	0.14	1.78	12.36

Source: Utopian Dept. of Information

Table 3   Average Vehicle Mileage 1971–81

Year	1971	1972	1973	1974	1975	1976	1977	1978	1979	1980	1981
Cars	7,800	NA*	NA				8,100	8,200	8,200	8,600	8,800
M/Cycles	3,400	NA	NA				2,400	2,300	2,300	2,300	2,300

*NA = Data not available.

Table 4   Total Utopian Sales – Motor Spirit – 1971–81 (in millions of tons)

Year	1971	1972	1973	1974	1975	1976	1977	1978	1979	1980	1981
Qty	6.74	7.21	7.73	8.67	9.39	10.02	10.85	11.56	11.96	12.75	13.52

Table 5   Consumer Spending in Utopia 1971–81 (Utopian dollars)

Year	Q_1	Q_2	Q_3	Q_4
1971	4,132	4,452	4,521	4,730
1972	4,366	4,787	4,774	4,998
1973	4,588	5,063	5,135	5,344
1974	4,953	5,377	5,462	5,724
1975	5,292	5,700	5,842	6,057
1976	5,666	6,126	6,138	6,317
1977	5,869	6,304	6,475	6,774
1978	6,474	6,662	6,872	7,237
1979	6,682	7,136	7,299	7,705
1980	7,111	7,704	7,989	8,412
1981	7,708	8,568	8,868	9,360

C. Essay Questions

C1   Compare and contrast the forecasting problems of:
    a. A company selling childrens' toys.
    b. A multinational oil company.
    c. An area health authority.
C2   Explain to a small businessman how analysis of past performance can help future results.
C3   Discuss how forecasting can help a management in its financial planning decisions.

Part IV Optimising Decisions
Chapter 13

Operational Research and Model Building

Objectives: *To identify the key features of, and steps in, the operational research approach to problem solving.*

Plan of the chapter:

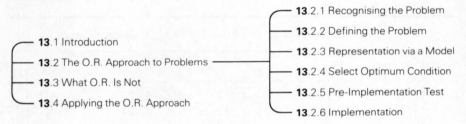

- **13**.1 Introduction
- **13**.2 The O.R. Approach to Problems
  - **13**.2.1 Recognising the Problem
  - **13**.2.2 Defining the Problem
  - **13**.2.3 Representation via a Model
  - **13**.2.4 Select Optimum Condition
  - **13**.2.5 Pre-Implementation Test
  - **13**.2.6 Implementation
- **13**.3 What O.R. Is Not
- **13**.4 Applying the O.R. Approach

13.1 Introduction

The purpose of this chapter is primarily to link previous and subsequent chapters by emphasising that the contents of both are required in a model building approach to problem solving.

Previous chapters have dealt with the presentation and analysis of data which is required to understand the problem more clearly and to distinguish between real and illusory relationships. The immediately previous chapter has discussed forecasting procedures that allow us to predict what the future values might be of such relationships. Subsequent chapters take the process of problem solving further and each chapter deals with a specific type of model through which this is done. This particular chapter discusses the general form of a model and model building methodology, crucial steps in the **operational research** approach. Operational research has a number of characteristics that distinguish it in approach from other so called 'scientific management' subjects. These are:

a. *An Interdisciplinary Approach.* Because of the increased complexity of business activity, people from many different backgrounds must be involved in the solution of particular problems.

b. *A Systems Approach*. The underlying causes of problems may be far removed from the symptoms. Thus one should try to avoid solving only one part of a problem (perhaps creating other problems) by looking at all interacting parts of the broader system.

c. *A Scientific Approach*. This involves conducting experiments with problem situation. In some cases this cannot be done under controlled laboratory conditions, and so O.R. practitioners conduct experiments using models of the real-world problems.

In Chapter 2, a typical decision-making sequence was suggested and the O.R. approach to problem solving is really an extension of this.

13.2 The O.R. Approach to Problems

The O.R. method has been defined by the O.R. Society as:

The attack of modern science on complex problems arising in the direction and management of large systems of men, machines, materials and money in industry, business, government and defence. The distinctive approach is to develop a scientific model of the system, incorporating measurement of factors such as chance and risk, in order to predict and compare the outcomes of alternative decisions, strategies and controls. The purpose is to help management determine its policy and actions scientifically.

The use of the word 'attack' illustrates the connection which still exists with the wartime experiences of O.R. The extension of this approach to business and other undertakings was a natural extension of the use of O.R. The above definition can be more easily illustrated by means of Fig. 13.1 below:

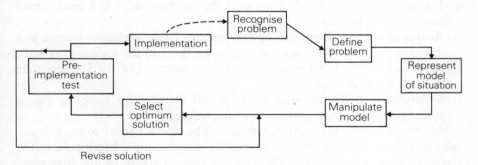

Fig. 13.1: The O.R. approach

The model contained in Fig. 13.1 is an extension of the decision-making sequence introduced in Chapter 2. It is worth looking at the key steps of the model in more detail.

13.2.1 Recognising the Problem

This particular stage in the O.R. method often causes the most headaches. The attitude that there is nothing wrong with my business and the inability to see the wood for the trees are prevalent in any organisation. It is also true that often familiarity breeds complacency. The O.R. team can be objective in this area. They have the ability to stand outside or above the organisation and have a look at the problem areas. Hence objectivity is an essential prerequisite to isolating problem areas.

A further difficulty lies in determining just what *is* the problem. The symptom of poor cash flow in a company might be the result of customers taking too long to pay, which might be a function of the supplier failing to send invoices quickly enough. This may in turn be a function of the paperwork system used or staff training.

13.2.2 Defining the Problem
This stage is an attempt to define the various interacting variables and to identify those which are important and those which are not. This is a crucial step as the solution depends on the correct identification of key factors. An incorrect appreciation at this stage will result in an inadequate solution, or even no solution at all.

First we think through the problem using any information available to us. As we have stressed before, each of us will 'see' problems differently and this will influence the information used. This underlines the importance of the multidisciplinary team and the systems approach, since the wide range of viewpoints can extend the problem beyond the level of curing symptoms.

13.2.3 Representation via a Model
Models are representations of real situations which are simplified to allow a more detailed study of the position. They can take three forms:
a. **Iconic models**: Small-scale replicas of the real features, e.g. a wind-tunnel model or a factory layout.
b. **Analogue models**: Representing real features by an analogous feature in a different medium, e.g. representing money flows in the economy by taps, pipes and bottles filled with liquid, or the portrayal of the London tube through a simple map.
c. **Symbolic models**: Representation of real features by symbols, e.g. a mathematical formula, graphs, flow diagrams etc.

Models are commonly used in business. The interaction of costs, volume, sales revenue and profit can be obtained by constructing a break-even chart. Here, the implications of, say, changing the price of goods, or installing plant to reduce costs are shown in the form of lines on a graph. Potentially catastrophic courses of action need cost no more than the price of a graph pad.

The concept of models is a simple one, but to actually visualise just what form a model should take is far more difficult in complex problems. This is where the high creativity value of a multidisciplinary team comes into its own.

In practice there are different types of problems which lend themselves to different types of model:

- Where the variable can be sufficiently defined a mathematical used.
- Where it is only possible to use a trial and error approach, and mathematical model is out of the question.
- Where a number of the variables are uncontrollable, such as cl arrivals at a filling station, then again a strict mathematical analysis is the question.

O.R. is therefore not exclusively a mathematical technique and might be more correctly termed a logical technique, where a complex problem/situation is simplified to a model base.

13.2.4 Select Optimum Condition

The word optimum means the best possible solution to the particular problem under consideration according to the organisation's objectives and strategy. This might mean most profitable, least cost, shortest distance, widest coverage etc. Thus the operation of a transport fleet might be reviewed in the light of minimising the total operating costs and not just fleet mileage.

13.2.5 Pre-implementation Test

It would be foolish to think that results established under laboratory conditions would necessarily be workable in the real-life situation. Rolls Royce discovered this to their cost with the use of carbon fibres in their RB 211 engine. The laboratory tests on these carbon fibres had proved them to be extremely strong. But in real life a shower of rain rendered them useless for the job they were supposed to do. Before a solution can be universally applied it must be pretested (ideally on a small scale).

If the pre-implementation test proves unsatisfactory then the solution will have to be revised.

13.2.6 Implementation

If on the other hand the solution is satisfactory then it can be implemented bearing in mind a number of factors.

- *The Problem of Change.* As with all changes, O.R. solutions must be introduced carefully. People are often unprepared to adjust to or accept change (e.g. there was the businessman who tried five teams of consultants before one team gave him the answer he was looking for).
- *The Problem of Communication.* O.R. is often misunderstood because of the barriers which exist between the two sides of the communication process. The young O.R. graduate with his academic approach and O.R. jargon versus the established and experienced manager with 'O' level (failed) maths. No wonder O.R. is often misapplied and misconceived by management.
- *The Problem of Interpersonal Relationships.* It is often said that 90 per cent of business consists of handling people. The O.R. man, often carried away by

his logical solution, tends to forget that people are not as logical as the tools of his trade or the computer. It is important that the operations researcher also takes into account the feelings of the people whose work pattern he is probably altering.

Inevitably implementation can throw up new problems, and so the cycle may well be repeated.

13.3 What O.R. is Not

So far, we have looked at what O.R. is, but it is worth briefly looking at what it *is not* as well. Operational research is a logical and scientific approach to decision making, encouraging a sounder approach to problem solving. However, one should stress that O.R. is not necessarily quantitative. It could readily be used in conjunction with iconic models such as Barnes Wallis' early experiments to assess the feasibility of the 'Dam Busters' bouncing bomb, which used a bathtub, elastic bands and table tennis balls.

O.R. is not infallible. It is called operational *research* and like all research activities has severe limitations. It may not provide a solution and a solution based on the toss of a coin may be better than no decision at all. But in the majority of cases O.R. will provide a solution which is more satisfactory than a rule of thumb approach.

Lastly, it must be noted that O.R. is *not* necessarily about finding the cheapest solution to problems. This is because the O.R. approach takes an overall, systems, viewpoint and hence certain areas of the system may in fact take longer or be more costly in order that the *system as a whole* is improved. Thus O.R. is not the same as work study. Work study is intended to improve the *efficiency* of an aspect of an organisation, whilst O.R. is intended to increase the *effectiveness* of an organisation.

13.4 Applying the O.R. Approach

The following chapters will look at a number of distinct problems in order to demonstrate the O.R. approach in action. Firstly, in Chapter 14 we will consider the planning of large-scale projects using network analysis. Then in Chapters 15 and 16 we will consider the problem of optimum resource allocation. Finally, in Chapter 17 we will consider problems where there is considerable variation, and we are attempting to simulate this variation as an aid to testing the effectiveness of decision.

Work Section

A. Revision Questions

A1 What is meant by 'an interdisciplinary approach' to problem solving?

A2 Why is a systems approach an important feature of O.R.?

A3 What are the key factors in a scientific approach to problem solving?

A4 What are the key stages in the O.R. approach?

A5 Why is problem recognition frequently seen to be the most difficult step of the approach?

A6 What is a model?

A7 Distinguish between iconic, analogue and symbolic models. Give an example of each.

A8 Does O.R. always use mathematical models?

A9 What is meant by the 'optimum solutions' to a problem?

A10 Why might the implemented solution differ from the optimum one decided from manipulation of the O.R. model?

C. Essay Questions

C1 Critically examine the concept of model building in relation to problem solving.

C2 Discuss how a systems approach might be used to improve the effectiveness of education in your own school or college.

Chapter 14

Network Analysis

Objectives: *To show how a network model of complex projects can result in more effective planning and control of decisions.*

Plan of the chapter:

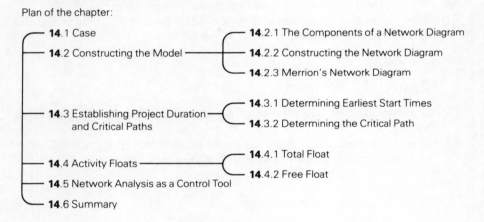
14.1 Case

Merrion was planning to extend a sports complex to increase facilities for swimming and the playing of squash, badminton and snooker, as well as providing ancilliary services such as social and changing areas. The Statistics Department have been asked to determine the best way of building the extension so as to get it finished in the shortest possible time.

The Department first noted that the project consists of fourteen major activities such as site clearance, foundations, basic structure erection etc. Some of these activities cannot be started until others have been completed. On the basis of this information they determined the order in which the activities should be done, and then determined likely durations for each of the fourteen activities. This is summarised below:

a. There are 14 main activities which are called A–N for short.

b. Activity   A B C D E F G H I J K L M N

★ Estimated

     duration   2 14 9 16 6 17 15 8 10 6 2 9 13 7

     (in days)

c.   i. A is the start of the project

     ii. C, B and D follow A

     iii. E follows B

     iv. H follows D

     v. F, G and J follow C

     vi. I follows E and F

     vii. K follows G and H

     viii. L and M follow J and K

     ix. N follows I and L

In addition to the construction industry, many other fields have the same problem of tying together interdependent activities. In teaching, the problem is doing the basics before more advanced work and yet maintaining interest. In the advertising world, it is pulling together all the elements of a major promotional campaign.

14.2 Constructing the Model

Having defined the problem in terms of the key interrelationships between the various activities, and their estimated durations, the team responsible for the study had to devise a model which would clearly show the sequence of activities and the duration.

A valuable model in such a case is the *network diagram*, and this forms the basis of network analysis. Network analysis is not the only name by which the approach is known, other names that have been used being 'Critical Path Analysis (CPA)' and the 'Project Evaluation and Review Technique (PERT)'.

The technique seems to have been first used when the Polaris missile system was being built in the USA in the middle 1950s. The original purpose for its use was to attempt to control and co-ordinate the activities of the vast number of subcontractors who were involved in making Polaris. In essence the management team decided to visually display, in network form, the activities of the various subcontractors. They paid particular attention to i. when their components would be needed; ii. what the duration of their work would be; iii. who would need to precede each contractor and who could follow on from that con-

---

★ See Question C4

tractor. The purpose of the network was to provide a master plan of a multi-activity and complex project that involved thousands of different contractors and tasks. The network was to provide the framework to plan these different activities, in a logical way, so that they formed a cohesive whole. It is claimed that this co-ordination not only avoided the chaos that might have occurred without such a technique but also saved something like two years in the development of the Polaris system.

14.2.1 The Components of a Network Diagram
The diagram is built up from three basic elements: activities, nodes and
★ dummies.

An **activity** is part of the project which consumes time and/or resources. Thus awaiting delivery of parts is an activity since time is consumed, and assembling the parts is another, consuming labour, materials *and* time. Activities are designated by arrows running from left to right, the length of the arrow having no significance.

A **node** is merely the start or finish of an activity (or activities) and is usually represented by a circle. It serves to separate activities.

A **dummy** is an activity of zero duration intended to emphasise logical dependencies.

14.2.2 Constructing the Network Diagram
Figure 14.1 below illustrates the statement 'Activity Q follows P' using the symbols described above.

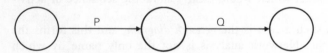

Fig. 14.1: Consecutive activities

Note how the direction of the arrow implies a strict logic in the analysis. Consider now the statements:
a. Activity Y can start only when both W *and* X are completed.
b. Activity Z can start only when X is completed.
At first glance, Fig. 14.2 (*a*) satisfies this, yet it *also* implies that Z cannot start until W is completed, as well as X.

To maintain the strict logic of the original statement, a dummy activity (represented by the dotted line in Fig. 14.2 (*b*)) must be used. A dummy has no duration and serves only to imply a logical dependency as mentioned earlier.

★ See Questions B1 and B2

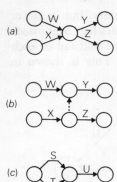

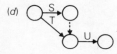

Fig. 14.2: Logical dependence via a dummy

Dummies may also be used to uniquely identify parallel activities as shown in Figs 14.2 (*c*) and (*d*).

Using these basic components, we can now look at Merrion's problem again.

14.2.3 Merrion's Network Diagram
Using the information on the fourteen activities in Section **14.1**, one can now construct a network for the Merrion project. The arrows and nodes will be interlinked according to whether a given activity precedes, follows or parallels other activities. Figure 14.3 shows a possible network diagram for the Merrion project.

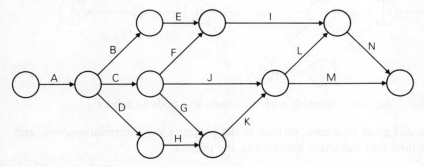

Fig. 14.3: Merrion's problem in network form

Note that *every* activity lies on a continuous path between the start and end of the project. There are no 'dead ends' since all activities must be completed if the project is to be concluded.

In this case, we have identified activities by means of letters, but in larger projects we would clearly run into problems once all 26 letters had been used. One often finds activities identified by the nodes at the head and tail of each activity arrow, each node being given a unique number. This is shown in Fig. 14.4 below.

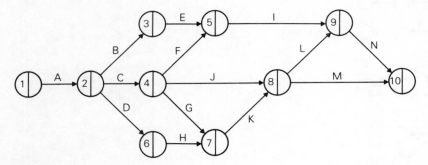

Fig. 14.4: Merrion's network numbered

Thus Activity A could also be designated 'Activity (1,2)' since it runs between 1 and 2. In this way, new activities can readily be introduced as the need arises. It is important that all activities, including dummies, are so covered.

We can now superimpose the durations of the fourteen activities on to the network diagram. It is conventional to write the duration below the arrow for each activity, as in Fig. 14.5.

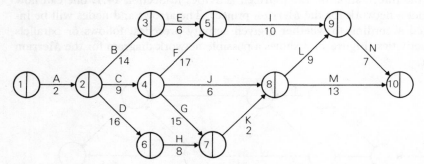

Fig. 14.5: Merrion's network with durations and node numbers

This model gives us a clear picture of the project's key interrelationships, and we can now find the likely duration of the project.

14.3 Establishing Project Duration and Critical Paths

We *could* list all possible paths through the network between node 1 and node 10 and find the time for each. The longest sequence will then determine the overall project duration. In more complex projects containing thousands of activities, this is clearly laborious and liable to error, so a better method needs to be sought.

14.3.1 Determining Earliest Start Times

Using Fig. 14.5, let us assume that the earliest that Activity A can start is day 0. Clearly B, C and D cannot start until A is finished, i.e. until day $(0 + 2) =$ day 2. Thus the **earliest start time (EST)** of B, C and D will be day 2.

In the same way E cannot start until both A and B are completed, i.e. by day $0 + 2 + 14 =$ day 16, and F, G and J cannot start until A and C end, i.e. by day $0 + 2 + 9 =$ day 11.

What now of node 5? Here, I cannot start until both E *and* F are completed. E will be finished by day $0 + 2 + 14 + 6 =$ day 22 but F won't be finished until day $0 + 2 + 9 + 17 =$ day 28. So the EST of I must be the longest time to node 5, i.e. day 28.

In general, whenever more than one arrow comes into a node, the EST will be a choice between a number of figures from which one should choose the highest to give the EST at the node under consideration.

You should now attempt to calculate the EST's for the Merrion project. Compare your results with those shown in Fig. 14.6 in which EST's are shown for each activity.

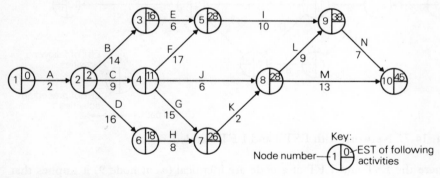

Fig. 14.6: EST's for Merrion's project

From Fig. 14.6, it is clear that the project will take 45 days to complete. We can now go on to determine which sequence of activities (*or critical path*) has determined this duration. Again, one could use trial and error, but again more complex networks will be a problem. (Please note that the method used to show node numbers, EST's and LFT's is only one of many in common use.)

14.3.2 Determining the Critical Path

Let us look at the *latest* times that activities could finish without extending the project duration of 45 days, (i.e. the **latest finish time – LFT –** for each activity).

If the project is not to over-run, activities M and N must be completed at node 10 by day 45. What now of activities I and L at node 9? Clearly they must be finished in time to allow N to be completed by day 45, i.e. by day (45 − 7) = day 38. Similarly, at node 5, E and F must be finished in time to allow I *and* N to be completed in time, so the LFT here will be day (45 − 7 − 10) = day 28.

At node 8, a slightly different problem is seen. Here, both J and K must be finished in sufficient time to allow both L and N, and M to be completed. L and N together take 16 days, whilst M takes only 13 days. Clearly J and K must be finished in time to allow the *longest* subsequent route (L + N) to be completed, so the LFT at node 8 must be day (45 − 9 − 7) = day 29.

So where there is more than one route back into a node, the mechanical rule is to take the *lowest* value of LFT obtained from the various routes. You should now calculate LFT's for the Merrion Project, and compare results with those shown in Fig. 14.7. Note that the LFT's for each node are shown in the bottom right-hand side of the circle.

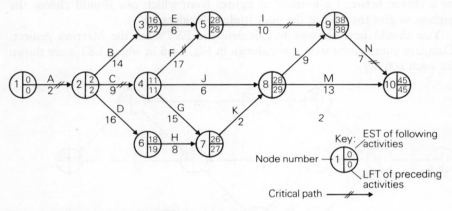

Fig. 14.7: Network with EST's and LFT's added

Where the EST and LFT at a node are identical (as at node 9) it implies that there can be no delay between finishing preceding activities and starting following ones unless the project's duration is to be extended. Thus N is a 'critical' activity in that any extra time spent on it will delay the whole project. In *every* network there will be *at least* one sequence of critical activities from start to finish – the **critical path** through the network. From Fig. 14.7 the critical path is A,C,F,I,N (or via nodes 1,2,4,5,9,10). All other activities are non-critical and could be extended to some extent without affecting the length of the project.

Before moving on, let us briefly summarise the steps covered to date:

★ **See Question B4**

a. Identify the key activities of the project.
b. For each activity, determine what activities must necessarily precede it and which must follow it.
c. Determine likely duration for each activity.
d. Construct a network diagram.
e. Determine the project duration by calculating the earliest start time (EST) for each activity.
f. Determine the critical path(s) through the network by calculating the latest finish time (LFT) for each activity and comparing these with EST. Critical activities are ones which must start as soon as the preceding activities are finished.

How much could non-critical activities over-run before affecting the project's duration? In order to answer this we must look at the **float** on activities.

14.4 Activity Floats

The float on an activity is a measure of how long that activity can over-run before affecting the project as a whole. There are several kinds of float but the two most important are **total float** and **free float**. Total Float is the longest the start of an activity can be delayed from its EST without delaying the project's duration. Free Float is the maximum period the start of an activity can be delayed from the EST without delaying the EST of any immediately following activity. Free Float relates therefore to just one activity whilst Total Float relates to a path. Total Float will always be numerically larger than or equal to the amount of Free Float.

14.4.1 Total Float
The total float of an activity is the difference between its earliest start time (EST) and latest start time (LST).

Total float = LST – EST

Figure 14.7 shows the EST, LFT and duration for each activity. Clearly, the LST will be (LFT – duration) so we can say that:

Total float = LFT – duration – EST.
In the case of activity E (between nodes 3 and 5), we have:

LFT of E (from node 5) = 28
Duration of E   =   6 days
EST of E (from node 3) = 16

Hence the total float on E is (28 – 6 – 16) = 6 days.
In the case of a critical activity such as N, the total float is (45 – 7 – 38) = 0. This is to be expected since, by definition, there can be no pause between activities on the critical path without delaying the whole project. All critical activi-

ties will show a total float of zero. (You might check this for the other critical activities on the network.)

As mentioned earlier, however, total float is not specific to an activity but to an uninterrupted path, and this affects how we may use it. You will recall that the total float on activity E was 6 days. What of the preceding activity, B? Here, total float is $(22 - 14 - 2) = 6$ days. Clearly we cannot delay both B and E by 6 days since to do so would cause the whole project to over-run. The total float of 6 days is available to all activities between nodes 2 and 5, $(= 28 - 6 - 14 - 2)$ and can be used in full *either* by B *or* by E, but not both. If B is delayed by 4 days, E can only fall behind by 2 days if the whole project is to be completed within 45 days.

To avoid this 'knock-on' effect, free float can be calculated for an activity.

14.4.2 Free Float
The free float on an activity is defined as the amount of delay possible on an activity without affecting the earliest start time of following activities. It is found by:

Free float = EST at end – duration – EST at beginning.

Hence in the case of activity B in Fig. 14.7, we have:

EST of activity E = 16
Duration of B   = 14
EST of activity B =   2

and the free float = $16 - 14 - 2 = \underline{0}$. Hence B cannot be extended at all without affecting the leeway available on E. The relationship between total and free float may be seen in Fig. 14.8 below.

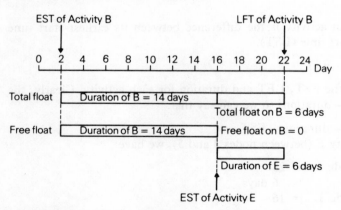

Fig. 14.8: Total and free float on activity B

★ See Question B5

You should now attempt to calculate the total and free floats for each activity in the Merrion Project. Check your findings with Fig. 14.9 below.

Activity		Event times at beginning		Event times at end		Duration	Total float	Free float
Nodes	Letter	LFT	EST	LFT	EST			
1–2	A	0	0	2	2	2	–	–
2–3	B	2	2	22	16	14	6	–
2–4	C	2	2	11	11	9	–	–
2–6	D	2	2	19	18	16	1	–
3–5	E	22	16	28	28	6	6	6
4–5	F	11	11	28	28	17	–	–
4–7	G	11	11	27	26	15	1	–
4–8	H	19	18	27	26	8	1	–
5–9	I	28	28	38	38	10	–	–
6–7	J	11	11	29	28	6	12	11
7–8	K	27	26	29	28	2	1	–
8–9	L	29	28	38	38	9	1	1
8–10	M	29	28	45	45	13	4	4
9–10	N	38	38	45	45	7	–	–

Fig. 14.9: Total and free float for Merrion project

The critical path is located where there is no total float, that is, via nodes 1, 2, 4, 5, 9 and 10. These activities form the continuous critical path through the network.

Figure 14.9 illustrates that some of the activities in Merrion's project have considerable float and this could be used to advantage. The most important of these may be to take men and resources off non-critical activities thus saving money. If the Council wanted to decrease the project time they would, of course, reallocate the resources to the critical activities; every day saved on a critical activity may mean a day saved on the overall length of the project. This gives a clue as to the value of the technique as an aid to control in project implementation by further manipulation of the model.

14.5 Network Analysis as a Control Tool

A great advantage of the O.R. approach is that it allows managers to experiment without spending vast amounts of time and money on abortive projects.

★ See Questions B6, B7

Network analysis is no exception, since it lends itself to the question 'What if . . .?' This is particularly valuable where delays might well occur, as in the construction industry. Suppose a firm was building a new school, and had prepared a network analysis model of the project. Even before work began, the model could be manipulated to ensure that optimum use was being made of plant and labour. 'What if we only use one excavator for the foundations?' might be answered by reference to the network. What subsequent effects might this decision have, and at what cost in time and money? 'What if the weather is too cold to pour concrete in January?' might suggest diverting workers elsewhere on the project to ensure that the hand-over date can still be kept despite the delay. Clearly continuous up-dating of the network is desirable once the project is under way: 'The steelwork is going to be late, so what can we do to keep our target completion date?'

The availability of packaged network analysis programs and cheap computer power means that even quite modest projects can benefit from the network approach. The intuitive guesses of the site foreman can be replaced by more objective analysis of alternative courses of action. The net result can be the far greater utilisation of material, financial and time resources.

14.6 Summary

Network analysis has been successfully used by many companies and continues to be used. Its strength is that it presents explicitly the logic used in planning a project. When this is done, other interested parties can discuss the logic and agree whether or not it is correct or needs to be changed. This is an important and often neglected aspect of decision making. By presenting the steps of the analysis in the fashion of network analysis you allow others to question the logic and hence spark off new insights into the problem thanks to the interdisciplinary and systems approaches of O.R.

In network analysis there is also the belief that by prior planning or control using networks, the project will ultimately be less expensive in both time and money. This is another feature of decision making that is sometimes neglected. Instead of following through an analysis to attempt to see what might happen and take the necessary avoiding action, managers will react to something after it has happened. It is always much better to proact than react.

★ See Question B9

Work Section

A. Revision Questions

A1 Distinguish between activities, nodes and dummies.

A2 Give two different illustrations of the use of dummy activities.

A3 How does one calculate the EST of an activity?

A4 Why must every activity form part of a continuous path through the network?

A5 If several activities converge at a node, how is the EST for following activities determined?

A6 What is the LFT of an activity?

A7 Give two methods of determining the critical path for a network.

A8 Distinguish between critical and non-critical activities.

A9 Need there be just one critical path through a network?

A10 Define total float and free float of an activity.

A11 How would you determine total float and free float for an activity?

A12 Is total float greater than, equal to, or less than free float?

A13 How can float calculation help to reduce project duration?

A14 Why can network analysis be thought of as an aid to control?

A15 State the key steps of the O.R. approach as applied to network analysis.

B. Exercises/Case Studies

B1 Draw the following network:
    A is the start of the project
    B starts when A is complete
    C follows B
    D starts at the same time as B
    E follows all other jobs.

B2 Draw a network using the following information:
    A is the start of the project
    B and E can start when A is complete
    C follows B
    F and G can start when E is complete
    D cannot start before C and F are complete and must be finished before J can start
    J also depends on the completion of H before it can start.

B3 A project consists of 12 activities shown in the accompanying table. The interrelationships between these activities are given below:

A and B can be performed in parallel
A must be performed before C, D and E
F cannot be started until D is finished
G follows C and D
F must be finished before H and I can be started
E and I precede J
G and H precede K
L depends on J and K being completed.

Activity	A	B	C	D	E	F	G	H	I	J	K	L
Duration days	4	18	2	4	9	1	7	3	2	5	4	

Draw a diagram for the above project and number the activities.

B4   Calculate the earliest start time, earliest finish time, latest start time, latest finish time and critical path analysis for the network of B3.

B5   Calculate the total and free float for each activity of the network obtained in B3 and B4. Why are the numbers generally smaller for free float?

B6   In the network below, a. determine the normal duration and critical path; b. calculate the cost of reducing the normal project duration by two, three and six days, and calculate the total cost of the project if it is carried out in the minimum possible time.

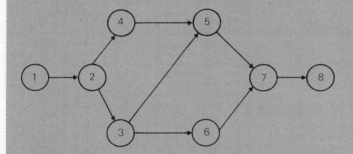

Activity	Normal duration	Shortest duration	Extra cost p/day saved (£)
1–2	4	3	25
2–3	5	3	50
2–4	4	3	15
3–5	8	4	5
3–6	5	3	20
4–5	7	3	15
5–7	7	5	30
6–7	7	4	15
7–8	4	2	40

B7 The following critical path network shows the sequence of 13 activities within a project. Each activity has a 'cost-slope' representing the amount that would be saved if a day more were allowed on its duration or the amount that would have to be incurred to obtain reduction of a day on that activity. Activity durations can only be increased or reduced by up to two days.

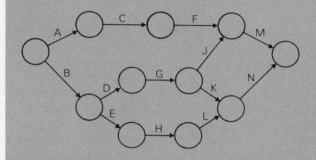

Activity	Duration (in days)	Cost slope	Activity	Duration (in days)	Cost slope
A	5	£400	G	8	£700
B	7	£800	H	3	£100
C	10	£500	J	11	£200
D	10	£300	K	6	£600
E	5	£400	L	4	£600
F	4	£400	M	8	£700
			N	9	£500

The project has also to bear £1,000 of general overheads for each day that it lasts.

a. Identify the critical path activities and calculate the total duration of the project.

b. Show that, by reducing the time spent on two activities, total project duration can be cut to 40 days while making a net cost saving (in total) of £3,000.

c. Discuss how you would further optimise the project, including any further information you might need.

(Cambridge Local Examinations A Level)

B8 *The Advertising Campaign*
Background: An agency is planning an advertising campaign to launch a new product. It will use posters, television and newspaper display. The

illustration for the newspaper advertisement will be devised while its accompanying text is being written and half-tone blocks will be made when both are ready. The blocks will then be sent to the newspapers, but only after the contract for press advertising has been negotiated. This part of the work is then finished.

The poster is to be designed and printed, after which, again subject to a satisfactory contract, it will be distributed (so completing this part of the campaign). The script for the television film is to be prepared while the contract for the film company is negotiated. The film is made after the script and contract are finalised. It must then be sent to the programme company for display, with whom a separate agreement must be reached beforehand.

As soon as all these preparations have been made a press conference is to be arranged at which the product will be officially launched. The agency allows a fortnight for drawing up a detailed plan of campaign; after this its negotiators begin work on the four contracts. Meanwhile the artists, copywriters and scriptwriters get on with such work as is possible.

Questions:

i. Draw a network for the campaign.

Timings

The following durations for individual activities have been estimated:

Activity	Duration (weeks)
Plan campaign	2
Press, write text	4
Press, illustration	4
Press, contract	3
Press, make blocks	2
Press, blocks to newspapers	1
Poster, design	8
Poster, contract	3
Poster, print	1
Poster, distribute	1
TV: write script	3
TV: contract for film-making	4
TV: contract display	3
TV: make film	6
TV: film to programme company	1
Arrange press conference	4

ii. Find the minimum time that must elapse before the launching of the product at the press conference and state the activities which fall upon the critical path.

iii. The advertising campaign is still being planned, but the television scriptwriters have already decided that the poster will play an important part in the film (it need not be printed but must be designed before the film can be shot).

What effect, if any, will this have on the launching date?

(Acknowledgements: London Business School)

B9 This project is scheduled to be completed in 180 days. The network and earliest and latest times are given below.

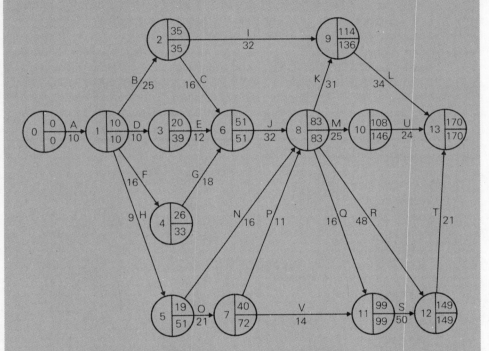

a. Can the project be completed in the scheduled time?

b. Examine the request of a department to be allowed to work overtime to reduce the duration time of 6–9 to 20 days.

c. Consider whether it is worthwhile to spend money purchasing a machine to reduce activity 1–2 to 20 days or spending the same money on a machine to reduce activity 8–12 to 20 days.

d. At the end of 50 days you are advised that the following activities are completed:

0–1	1–5
1–2	2–6
1–3	3–6
1–4	4–6

but material shortage will not permit activity 5–8 to start for another 20 days. Assess the effect of this.

   e. If 4–6 is increased to 32 days, what effect will this have on the project duration? Is there a new critical path?

B10 For the network in B9:

   a. Calculate the total float and the free float for each activity in the network shown.

   b. Activity C is composed of three jobs which must be undertaken one after the other. For each there is a probability of $\frac{1}{4}$ that it takes 2 days, of $\frac{1}{2}$ that it takes 3 days and of $\frac{1}{4}$ that it takes 4 days. Assuming statistical independence, find the probability that the duration of C is 6 or 7 days.

B11 *Steam Pipe Overhaul*

An overhead steam pipeline is found to be in need of repair and overhaul. In order to diagnose the fault, it is necessary to shut off steam, allow the line to cool, erect scaffolding, strip the lagging and then examine, measure and sketch the defective portion of the line. Then a list of materials

---

Activities Involved

Deactivate pipe	1 day
Erect scaffolding	4 days
Strip lagging	2 days
Examine, measure and sketch	2 days
Prepare material list	2 days
Obtain cutting and welding equipment	7 days
Remove all pipe and valves	10 days
Obtain lifting gear	4 days
Obtain new pipe	6 days
Assemble new pipe	1 day
Place new pipe	2 days
Obtain new valves	8 days
Weld pipe	2 days
Fit valves	3 days
Pressure test	1 day
Obtain lagging	5 days
Remove lifting gear	1 day
Lag pipe	4 days
Force-dry lagging	1 day
Obtain paint	5 days
Paint	6 days
Clean up and start	2 days
Remove scaffold	3 days

is drawn up to enable new pipe, valves, lagging and paint to be obtained. The removal of the defective pipe requires special cutting and welding equipment to be obtained.

Upon receipt of the materials, the new pipe can be assembled at ground level and then lifted into place using lifting gear (which must be obtained). Once in place, it is welded and the new valves can be fitted. The pipe is then pressure-tested, lagged and painted. In order to accelerate the drying on the lagging steam is passed down the pipe. Whilst the area is being cleared up, the pipe is put into use. The lifting gear can be removed after the pressure test.

Questions:
  i. Draw the network.
 ii. Analyse the network.
iii. Deduce the earliest time that the lifting gear will be available for other purposes.
 iv. Although the pipe is faulty it can still be used. Once the overhaul has started, will it be possible to delay the deactivation of the line without affecting the total time for the overhaul?

C. Essay Questions

C1 'CPA is about putting activities into the right order.' Do you agree that this is the essence of the technique?
C2 Discuss how CPA helps managers to be more effective decision makers.
C3 In what way does CPA make use of:
    a. The systems approach?
    b. The interdisciplinary approach?
C4 How might the durations used in the Merrion study have been deduced? Discuss how use of the Normal distribution might give more representative durations.

Chapter 15

Blending

Objectives: *To demonstrate that optimum resource allocation can be achieved using a mathematical model based on equation of inequalities.*

Plan of the chapter:

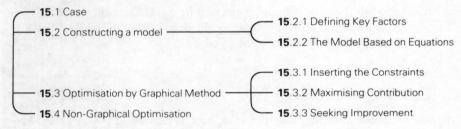

15.1 Case

Merrion's Social Services Department runs a sheltered workshop where physically and mentally handicapped people can work in closely supervised surroundings. The workshop is run on business lines and is required to show a profit. At present, two products are made, a toy bear and a glove puppet. Both products 'compete' for resources in that some operations and materials are common to both products. Each of the products makes a positive contribution to the workshop's fixed overheads, and the key question is what mix of bears and puppets would yield the highest possible contribution? The O.R. team has been asked to offer advice.

15.2 Constructing a Model

As with any problem to be tackled by the O.R. approach, the problem must first be defined.

15.2.1 Defining Key Factors

First, the O.R. team had to find out what resources were available and what the limitations on each was. Then, the requirements of each product for each resource needed to be determined. The team's findings are summarised in Fig. 15.1 below.

Resource	One bear requires	One puppet requires	Maximum available/ week
Man-hours	4 man-hr	2 man-hr	1,200 man-hr
Furry fabric	1 m^2	0.25 m^2	200 m^2
Stuffing	50 g	nil	7.5 kg
Packaging	1 bag	1 bag	750 bags

Fig. 15.1: Resource availability

Since it is known that the workshop is aiming to maximise total **contribution** the team had to find the contribution on each bear and puppet sold – £2.50 per bear and £1.00 per glove puppet.

15.2.2 A Model Based on Equations

Let us assume that the relationship between the limitation on resources is a linear one. That is to say that they are related in a similar manner to the general form:

$y = mx + c$ where y and x are variable quantities and m and c are constants.

A graphical plot of this relationship would give a straight line. This is a vital assumption if we are to make use of the following mathematical model. We can express the various constraints on resources by means of mathematical formulae. Let us suppose that B bears were made in a week and G glove puppets. For the constraint of man-hours this would require:

4B + 2G man-hr.

This cannot exceed 1,200 man-hr however (but could be anywhere between 0 and 1,200), so we could say that:

4B + 2G ≤ 1200.

Repeating the process for the other constraints gives:

Fabric:	B + 0.25G ≤	200
Stuffing:	50B	≤ 7,500
Packaging:	B + G	≤	750

We can further state that the contribution (C) at the outputs will be:

$C = 2.5B + 1.0G.$

The requirement is that C should be as large as possible subject to the other constraints being met.

In this example, there are only two competing variables – the outputs of bears and glove puppets – so we could express the various relationships on a graph having outputs of bears and puppets as the two axes. (Alternatively one could use an algebraic method, and this would have to be done were there three or more competing products. This will be considered later.)

15.3 Optimisation by Graphical Method

We can now plot the information on the graphical model.

15.3.1 Inserting the Constraints

Let us consider the man-hours constraint first. The relationship between bears, puppets and the total man-hours available was summarised in the relationship:

$$4B + 2G \leqslant 1,200.$$

In the limiting case, the hours used will be 1,200. Since we have assumed a linear relationship between bears and puppets we could produce any mixture of bears and puppets given by the relationship:

$$4B + 2G = 1,200.$$

If no puppets were made, G would equal zero, and so:

$$4B = 1,200, \text{ and hence } B = \underline{300}.$$

Similarly, if no bears were made:

$$2G = 1,200 \text{ and hence } G = \underline{600}.$$

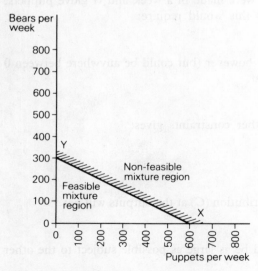

Fig. 15.2: The man hours constraint

In figure 15.2, the line XY represents the maximum possible mix of bears and puppets that could be made. Thus, whilst 400 puppets and 100 bears could be made, a mix such as 700 puppets and 200 bears could not. The triangle formed by the axes and the line XY represents the area in which feasible mixtures can be obtained.

The limitations on fabric, stuffing and packaging can now be added in the same way as shown in Figure 15.3.

Fig. 15.3: All constraints included

From this we can see:

- That the region in which feasible solutions may be found is now reduced to the five-sided area.
- That the stuffing constraint is shown by a line parallel to the 'puppets' axis. This is because the maximum number of bears that can be made is constant for all outputs of puppets, as stuffing is only used for bears. (Mathematically the line is expressed $50B = 7,500$, which contains no value for puppet output.)

Of the many feasible mixtures possible, which will satisfy the requirement of maximum contribution?

15.3.2 Maximising Contribution
In Section 15.2.2, the contribution to fixed costs (C) was shown to be:

$C = 2.5B + 1.0G.$

Thus if C were, say, £250, we can plot the line since:

when $B = O$, $G = 250$
when $G = O$, $B = 100$.

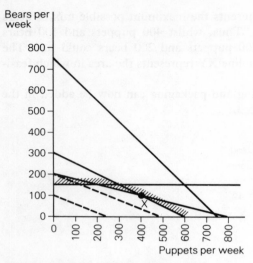

Fig. 15.4: Finding the optimum mixture

Higher values of *C* result in lines parallel to the one for £250, but further from the origin. A selection is shown as dotted lines in Fig. 15.4.

It may be seen that the maximum possible contribution consistent with the various constraints will be the one associated with the mixture at point X. Point X corresponds to an *optimum* of 100 bears and 400 puppets, and this mixture yields a contribution of

$$(100 \times £2.5) + (400 \times £1.00) = \underline{£650}$$

which is the *optimum* contribution under the constraints given.

15.3.3 Seeking Improvements

A great bonus of the graphical method is that it clearly shows the way in which the various constraints operate. If the diagram were to be made from coloured strings on a board, we could readily move the lines to check new possibilities and show even the non-numerate person the essence of the situation.

From Fig. 15.4, we can see that increasing the supply of stuffing or packaging will not increase the maximum contribution. Increasing the total supply of man-hours would allow maximum contribution to rise however, (as would decreasing the man-hours required to make each unit through productivity improvements).

Whilst the example in Section **15.2** considered the maximisation of contribu-

---

★ See Question B1

★ tion, other problems might well require the minimisation of a quantity. An example might be the minimisation of cost of production of meat pies. (In the language of the mathematician, the factor to be optimised is known as the *index of performance*.)

15.4 Non-graphical Optimisation

Whilst the graphical method used in Section 15.3 has the advantage of showing the key factors very clearly, graphical solutions may not always be feasible. This is because:

a. There are too many constraints to allow a clear graph to be constructed, even though only two demands compete for resources;. or

b. There are more than two demands competing for resources. For example, if the workshop made bears, puppets, dolls and cushions a four axis graph is impossible.

In such cases, solutions based on algebra may be used. The *Simplex Method* devised to cope with such problems makes use of a fact which is readily seen from Fig. 15.4 – whenever there is a feasible region, the optimum solution will always lie at the corner of that region (or at two corners if the contribution line had the same slope as one of the constraint lines).

No detailed coverage of the Simplex Method will be given here, but it is important to realise that the method consists of a series of separate steps, and is thus ideally suited to a computer program. Whilst the method can be applied manually, the larger scale of typical problems means that the use of computers can speed up the examination of alternative possibilities. The ability to optimise the allocation of many resources to a large number of competing demands clearly has wide applications. The ingredients for mixtures in industry (foodstuffs, paint, animal feeds etc) can be optimised for minimum overall cost. Profit from a factory can be maximised if sales objectives are more in tune with the ability of plant to manufacture (or vice versa). As with O.R. approaches, the main difficulty lies in seeing that a suitable problem exists in the first place.

★ See Question B6

Work Section

A. Revision Questions

A1 What is a linear relationship between two variables?

A2 Explain the meaning of the mathematical statement $x + 2y \leqslant 10$.

A3 Explain the meaning of the mathematical statement $x + 2y \geqslant 10$.

A4 Why can one not use graphical solutions in cases where there are more than two demands competing for a resource?

A5 In addition to knowing the maximum values of each resource available, what other two pieces of information are needed before a model can be constructed?

A6 Show graphically the following lines:

$$3x + y = 9$$
$$2x + 4y = 8$$

A7 Show graphically the following statements:

$$3x + y \leqslant 9$$
$$2x + 4y \geqslant 8$$

A8 What is the difference between the graphs obtained in your answers to A6 and A7?

A9 Explain what is meant by 'a feasible area of solution' on a graph similar to Fig. 15.4.

A10 What can be said about any optimum solution obtained by a graphical blending method?

B. Exercise/Case Studies

B1 Using Fig. 15.4 assess the effect of the following changes on the optimum solution:
a. The maximum supply of man-hours increased. by 10 per cent.
b. The man-hours required to produce one bear was halved.
c. The contribution on each bear sold was increased to £4.00.

B2 A furniture company manufactures tables, chairs and bookcases. These are made out of hardwood and softwood, and each requires a certain number of man-hours to make. Each week there are 1,500 feet of hard-wood, 1,000 feet of softwood and 800 man-hours available. The profit on a table is £1, on a chair 50p, and on a bookcase £1. The requirements for hardwood, softwood and man-hours for each item are given in the table below.

Item	Hardwood (ft)	Softwood (ft)	Man-hours
Table	4	2	1
Chair	1	3	2
Bookcase	6	3	3

a. Show that it is possible for the company to make 125 tables, 100 chairs and 150 bookcases in a week, and find the total profit on this output.
b. If the production of bookcases in a week is fixed at 150, by how much can the production of chairs be increased if the production of tables is reduced to 50?

(Attempt a solution first without a graphical plot, and then using one.)

B3 A woodworking firm makes two products A and B which are processed on each of three machines in the times summarised below:

Machine	Hours to produce 1,000 units of product		Capacity of machine in hours
	A	B	
1	4	6	240
2	8	4	240
3	2	3	150

Set this up as a blending problem and solve graphically if the profit on a unit of A is 2.4p and on B is 3.0p and you wish to maximise profits.

B4 Two products, A and B, are each processed in succession on two types of machine, X and Y. Each unit of A takes 20 minutes on an X machine and 1 hour on a Y machine; a B unit takes half an hour on X and half an hour on Y. Selling prices and variable costs are:

	Product A	Product B
Selling price per unit	£10	£19
Variable cost per unit	£ 8	£13

There are two machines of type X and four of type Y, each machine with a yearly capacity of 2,500 hr. Each year, fixed costs of £30,000 must be covered and the maximum market size for A is 9,000 units and for B 8,000 units, at present.

Show all the constraints on a graph and find the optimal production plan assuming that all production is sold immediately; also calculate the annual net profit.

B5   A firm makes two kinds of leather belts. Belt A is a high-quality belt and belt B is a lower quality. The respective profits are £0.40 and £0.30 per belt. Each belt of type A requires twice as much time as a belt of type B and, if all belts were of type B the company could make 1,000 per day. The supply of leather is sufficient for only 800 belts per day (both A and B combined). Belt A requires a fancy buckle, and only 400 per day are available. There are only 700 buckles a day available for belt B.

Assuming that the firm wishes to maximise profits, calculate an optimal production programme by the use of a graph.

B6   Three types of paint A, B and C are each made from the same chemicals W, X, Y and Z. The amounts required for 10 tons of each are as follows:

	W	X	Y	Z
A	3	2	3	2
B	1	4	4	1
C	4	3	2	1

The weekly supply of chemicals is limited to 200 tons per W, 170 tons of X, 160 tons of Y and 70 tons of Z. Profits of £5 a ton are estimated for A, £6 a ton for B and £4 a ton for C.

Find the maximum weekly profit that can be made if:

  i. only type A is manufactured
 ii. only type B is manufactured
iii. only type C is manufactured
 iv. some of both B and C is manufactured
  v. exactly 50 tons of A are manufactured plus some of B and C.

Use a graphical method to solve iv. and v.

C. Essay Questions

C1   Discuss two examples where the ideas of blending could be applied in practice.

C2   Explain how the graphical presentation of a blending problem can help even a non-numerate manager understand the essence of the situation.

Chapter 16

The Transportation Technique

Objectives: *To show how large systems having many supply and demand points can be modelled in order to make the optimum use of the facilities available.*

Plan of the chapter:

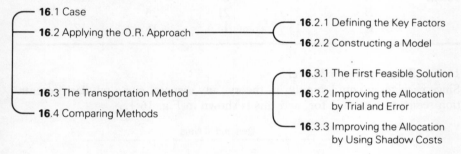

- **16**.1 Case
- **16**.2 Applying the O.R. Approach
  - **16**.2.1 Defining the Key Factors
  - **16**.2.2 Constructing a Model
- **16**.3 The Transportation Method
  - **16**.3.1 The First Feasible Solution
  - **16**.3.2 Improving the Allocation by Trial and Error
  - **16**.3.3 Improving the Allocation by Using Shadow Costs
- **16**.4 Comparing Methods

16.1 Case

The refuse collection service in Merrion has four disposal sites in its area, and waste from three towns is tipped there. The capacity of each site is limited by considerations of access and the ability of the installed plant to process the waste. At present, refuse vehicles tend to discharge their loads at the nearest disposal site but this has caused overloading at some sites and under-utilisation of vehicles. Not only that, but some vehicles have to be diverted to another site if the first is saturated, so fleet mileages have been rising. Can the routing of vehicles be improved so that the overall fleet mileage can be minimised? The systems approach implied here seems to lend itself to the O.R. approach. Whilst distribution systems are obvious candidates for O.R. analysis, any supply/demand situation (e.g. warehouse management in retailing) might apply since the choice is to be made between competing alternative sources and demands.

16.2 Applying the O.R. Approach

Problems of the above type can be dealt with using a model based on **linear programming**. In particular, the **'transportation** method' would be well-suited here. But first the problem needs to be defined.

16.2.1 Defining the Key Factors
The sites at Debenham, Earley, Foxton and Grassington can cope with 50, 60, 70 and 95 loads weekly whilst the residents of Anderley, Broughton and Chapeltown produce 275 loads weekly – 70, 90 and 115 respectively. The costs of transporting one load between the towns and sites are shown below (in £s).

		Sites			
		D	*E*	*F*	*G*
Towns	*A*	17	20	13	12
	B	15	21	26	25
	C	15	14	15	17

16.2.2 Constructing a Model
Since each town could supply, in theory, any disposal site a tabular presentation seems to be called for, and this is shown in Fig. 16.1.

Fig. 16.1: A tabulation of supply and demand

In Fig. 16.1 we can see that the total supply from each town is shown in the extreme right hand column, whilst the bottom row shows the total demand at each site. A quick check shows that total demand for the whole system does not exceed total supply and thus a feasible solution can be obtained.

We can now incorporate the cost of transporting one load via each route into the tabulation as shown in Fig. 16.2 below.

		Demand				
		D	E	F	G	
	A	17	20	13	12	70
Supply	B	15	21	26	25	90
	C	15	14	15	17	115
		50	60	70	95	

Fig. 16.2: Tabulation with route costs inserted

★ If the total supply available exceeded the total demand (or vice versa), we could assume a dummy demand (or supply) point, and so insert another column (or row), having zero route costs. The dummy therefore takes up any imbalance in the system.

In using the costs for each route in this way, we are really assuming a linear relationship between the total cost of using a route and the number of loads using that route. For example, if we send loads along route AD, one load would cost £17, two loads £34 and so on. The model therefore is another use of the linear programming approach first mentioned in Chapter 15.

We now have a model which we can manipulate to determine the optimum solution(s). Whilst we could use a blind 'hit and miss' technique and hope to hit on the best allocation, we would be better advised to follow a series of well-defined stages.

16.3 The Transportation Method

16.3.1 A First Feasible Solution
Let us make an arbitrary first allocation of loads between towns and sites. Suppose we decide to start at the top left-hand corner of the table (which we can call cell AD). D can cope with 50 loads whilst A could produce 70. Let D be completely supplied from A. The surplus 20 loads from A can go to E, which

★ See Question B2

	D	E	F	G	
A	17 50	20 20	13	12	70
B	15	21 40	26 50	25	90
C	15	14	15 20	17 95	115
	50	60	70	95	

Fig. 16.3: A first feasible solution

can cope with a total of 60. Thus E can take 40 from B . . . and so on. Figure 16.3 shows the result of this initial arbitrary allocation.

16.3.2 Improving the Allocation by Trial and Error

Is the allocation in Fig. 16.3 the best one? We develop a systematic way of answering this later, but for the moment, we will do so by trial and error. Sending vehicles from C to D rather than A to D will reduce the cost by $(17 - 15) = £2$ per load so sent. But if only *one* load is so re-routed, we have exceeded the capacity of C to supply all four sites, whilst failing to dispose of all loads coming from A. Thus we must balance any move from A to C by a corresponding one from C to A. Every load moved from CG to AG will result in a saving of $(17 - 12) = £5$, and a quick check suggests that we can move 50 loads in this way at an overall saving of £350, thus resulting in a second feasible solution shown in Fig. 16.4.

	D	E	F	G	
A	17	20 20	13	12 50	70
B	15	21 40	26 50	25	90
C	15 50	14	15 20	17 45	115
	50	60	70	95	

Fig. 16.4: A second feasible solution

Further pairs of moves can be spotted in the same way, and a possible sequence of such moves is given below.

| Move 1 load: | | Cost change | Net cost | | No. of | Total |
From	*To*	*per load (£)*	*change (£)*	×	*loads moved*	*= saving (£)*
AE	CE	– 6				
CF	AF	– 2	–8		20	160
BF	CF	–11				
CD	BD	0	–11		50	550
CF	AG	– 5				
AF	AC	+ 2	–3		20	60

Note how the last move shows a net saving of £3 per load although one part of the move shows and *increase* in cost. This is because we are trying to reduce the cost for the system *as a whole*.

At this point, we have the situation shown in Fig. 16.5. Any further attempt to move loads results either in a net *increase* in costs or no net change. So this is the *optimum* solution for the situation under discussion, with a total fleet costs of £4,185 as opposed to the £4,305 of the first allocation of Fig. 16.3.

	D	E	F	G	
A	17	20	13	12 70	70
B	15 50	21 40	26	25	90
C	15	14 20	15 70	17 25	115
	50	60	70	95	

Fig. 16.5: Optimum allocation

Whilst the trial and error method can lead to a successful solution, it can be time consuming to check all possible moves in large problems. In addition, it is hard to see when an optimum solution has been obtained. To help overcome these problems, an alternative method based on the concept of **'shadow costs'** has been devised.

	D	E	F	G	
A	17 50	20 20	13	12	70
B	15	21 40	26 50	25	90
C	15	14	15 20	17 95	115
	50	60	70	95	

Fig. 16.6: A first feasible solution

16.3.3 Improving the Allocation using Shadow Costs

Let us return to the first feasible solution (Fig. 16.3) of Section **16.3.1**.

The key assumption of the shadow cost method is that each *used* route cost is made up of two components:
  i. A cost of despatch from towns (say £a, £b, £c, for A, B and C).
★ ii. A cost of receipt at sites (say £d, £e, £f, £g for D, E, F and G).
A further requirement of the method, based on mathematical requirements, is that *only m + n – 1 routes are used* (where *m* = number of sources, *n* = number of receipt points). In this case, we must use $3 + 4 - 1 = 6$ routes. Hence the route cost of AE (£17 per load) could be considered to be £a + £e. All other routes used in the first feasible solution can now be similarly treated giving:

$$a + d = £17$$
$$a + e = £20$$
$$b + e = £21$$
$$b + f = £26$$
$$c + f = £15$$
$$c + g = £17$$

Let us now *arbitrarily* make the despatch cost for one town (say A) equal to £0. Since we now know the value of a, the first equation above gives a value of £17 for d. Continuing with this substitution gives:

$a = £0, b = £1, c = -£10, d = £17, e = £20, f = £25, g = £27$.

We can now show the shadow costs associated with this first allocation as in Fig. 16.7.
Let us now consider the *unused* routes in Fig. 16.7. In the case of AF the

★ See Question B8

	Shadow costs	D	E	F	G	
		17	20	25	27	
A	0	17 50	20 20	13	12	70
B	1	15	21 40	26 50	25	90
C	−10	15	14	15 20	17 95	115
		50	60	70	95	

Fig. 16.7: First feasible solution with shadow costs inserted

actual route cost is £13 per load whilst the assumed route cost (£a + £f) is (£0 + £25) = £25. We will call the difference between actual and assumed costs the *opportunity cost* of the unused route, in this case (£13 − £25) = −£12. This means that every load sent via this route will reduce the overall cost by £12. A positive value of the opportunity cost would mean that loads sent via the route in question would *add* to the overall cost.

Now look at each unused route in turn:

Route	Actual route cost/load (£)	− Assumed route cost/load (£)	= Opportunity cost (£)
AF	13	0 + 25 = 25	−12
AG	12	0 + 27 = 27	−15
BD	15	1 + 17 = 18	− 3
BG	25	1 + 27 = 28	− 3
CD	15	−10 + 17 = 7	8
CE	14	−10 + 20 = 10	4

We shall clearly aim to use route AG to the full as this gives the maximum potential for cost reduction. Let us reallocate *x* loads to this route. This will mean that we must amend the quantities sent via other routes accordingly to preserve the overall supply/demand constraints. This is shown in Fig. 16.8 (which also shows the opportunity costs for unused routes in the bottom right hand corner of each unused cell).

		D	E	F	G	
	Shadow costs	17	20	25	27	
A	0	17 50	20 20−x	13 (−12)	12 x (−15)	70
B	1	15 (−3)	21 40+x	26 50−x	25 (−3)	90
C	−10	15 (8)	14 (4)	15 20+x	17 95−x	115
		50	60	70	95	

Fig. 16.8: First solution with opportunity costs added and x loads sent via

We should aim to send as many loads as possible via route AG and hence maximise x. But remember that we cannot have x so large that it results in a *negative* number of loads going via another route, nor can we have (as now) seven routes in use. We must therefore eliminate one of the routes at present in use and inspection shows that this will be AE. (Eliminating BF would put −30 loads via AD, which is nonsense.)

We can send a maximum of 20 loads via AG, and the new allocation – a second feasible solution – is shown in Fig. 16.9. Note that we still use only (m + n − 1) routes as before.

	D	E	F	G	
A	50			20	70
B		60	30		90
C			40	75	115
	50	60	70	95	

Fig. 16.9: Second feasible solution

We can now check whether further improvement is possible by re-calculating the shadow costs for each route *now* being used and hence the new opportunity cost for unused routes. Any further negative opportunity costs suggests that further cost reduction is possible, and so an improved third solution is feasible.

This process is continued until either:

- All opportunity costs are positive, in which case any further reallocation would result in an increase in total cost.
- All opportunity costs are positive or zero, in which case any further reallocation would result in an increase as above, or an alternative optimum solution having the same cost.

Figure 16.10 below shows the final tabulation at which the optimum solution has been reached.

	Shadow costs	D 3	E 9	F 10	G 12	
A	0	17 (14)	20 (11)	13 (3)	12 / 70	70
B	12	15 / 50	21 / 40	26 (4)	25 (1)	90
C	5	15 (7)	14 / 20	15 / 70	17 / 25	115
		50	60	70	95	

Fig. 16.10: Final optimum solution

You will see that the allocation obtained in Fig. 16.10 is exactly the same as the one obtained by trial and error in Fig. 16.5. In either case, if the refuse loads are sent according to the allocation, a minimum overall cost will be achieved, provided that the constraints and costs do not change. If they do, a new allocation may need to be determined.

16.4 Comparing Methods

At first sight, the shadow cost method of Section **16**.3.3 seems more complex and time consuming than the trial and error approach. This may be true for relatively simple situations of the type considered, but when larger systems of tens of sources and perhaps hundreds of receipt points are under review, the logical, step-by-step approach of the shadow cost method is invaluable. This is because the rules governing the process can readily be converted into a computer program. The spread of cheap computer power means that such analysis is no longer the province only of the Ministry of Defence or very large companies.

The methods are not confined to transport fleets. Any supply and demand system, such as stock in a warehouse, may be so treated. (In such a case, the route costs might be replaced by storage costs.) This re-emphasises the importance of being able to spot the *key* factors in a problem, and showing their interrelationship in a suitable model.

Work Section

A. Revision Questions

A1 Can the transportation method be used if a. total demand exceeds total supply? b. total demand equals total supply? c. total demand is less than total supply?

A2 To what does the 'linear' in 'linear programming' apply in the transportation technique?

A3 How would you set out a tabulation for a situation in which there were three sources, four demand points and total demand was less than total supply?

A4 What do you understand by the term 'first feasible solution'?

A5 What assumption concerning route costs is made when the shadow cost method is used?

A6 If a system has m sources and n receipt points, how many routes must be used to allow shadow costs to be determined?

A7 How does one calculate the shadow costs for each source and receipt point?

A8 What is the significance of the opportunity cost for each unused route?

A9 How does one know that an allocation is the optimum using the shadow cost method?

A10 What is the significance of an allocation in which the opportunity cost of unused routes are either positive or zero?

B. Exercises/Case Studies

B1 A company must ship from three factories to four warehouses. The transportation cost per unit from each factory to each warehouse, the requirements of each warehouse, and the capacity of each factory are:

| Warehouses | Cost of transport/unit (£) | | | Warehouse requirement |
	F1	F2	F3	
A	11	6	8	100
B	7	3	8	200
C	5	3	8	450
D	4	5	6	400
Factory capacity	600	400	150	

Using the transportation technique, find the minimum cost of transportation.

B2 Using the data of B1: Suppose warehouse B goes out of business. This means that there is now an excess factory capacity of 200 units. Find the minimum cost transportation schedule. How could you handle the case where total warehouse requirements exceed total factory capacity?

B3 Two comparable jobs are to be loaded on to the milling shop of an engineering company and will require 14 and 23 hr of process time respectively. Three of the vertical milling machines are available with capacities of 16, 18 and 3 hr respectively. The operating costs of each type of machine in £ per hour provide constant returns to scale and are as follows:

	Machines		
Jobs	M1	M2	M3
J1	3	4	2
J2	1	1	5

Allocate the machines to jobs in order to minimise total operating costs.

B4 For the following tables discuss the problem of calculating shadow and opportunity costs in the light of the number of cells in use.

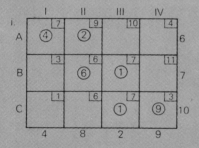 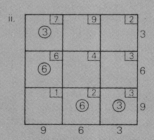

B5 A firm has two factories that ship to three regional warehouses. The costs of transportation in £ per unit are:

	F1	F2
W1	9	4
W2	11	3
W3	3	8

The warehouse needs are 13, 7 and 10 units respectively and 18, 16 units are available in F1 and F2 respectively. Using any method you like minimise the total transportation costs.

B6 Because of the imbalance between the needs of the factories and the warehouse an extra warehouse W4 has been built with transportation costs per mile of 6 and 4 respectively from F1 and F2. The warehouse capacity is 4 units. Using this and the data given in B5:

a. Calculate the minimum total cost by any method.

b. Use the transportation technique to minimise total transportation costs.

B7 Factory 1 is modern and produces for £1 per unit. Factory 2 is old and has a variable manufacturing cost of £2 per unit. Using the data of B6 and the additional data with respect to manufacturing costs, calculate the minimum total variable cost plus cost of transportation, using the transportation technique, and determine the optimal allocation which minimises costs.

B8 Three factories are located in London, Birmingham and Bristol. The organisation has a distributive system which serves market areas in Liverpool, Hull, Newcastle, Reading and Cambridge. The three factories have produced capacities of 19,000, 28,000 and 25,000 units respectively. The five distribution points have demands upon the factories of 11,000, 13,000, 7,000, 17,000 and 24,000 respectively. The cost of transporting one unit (£) is given in the table below:

	Liverpool	Hull	Newcastle	Reading	Cambridge
London	42	42	44	40	44
Birmingham	34	42	40	46	48
Bristol	46	44	42	48	46

a. Determine a feasible solution and the transportation cost associated with it.

b. How many routes have you used?

c. Why is it important to have seven routes used with respect to the transportation technique's use in this problem.

d. Using the transportation technique calculate the total minimum transport cost of the system.

B9 A company produces four different qualities of a product with total sales of 400 units per week. Three types of machine are used; there are 14 of type A, 12 of type B and 8 of type C, and every machine is used for 50 hr per week (assume no breakdowns). The problem is to allocate the different qualities of the product to the different types of machine in order to minimise costs.

With the intention of applying linear programming techniques the following information was collected:

Quality	I	II	III	IV
Weekly demand	50	150	100	100
Machine-hours to make 1 unit	14	4	3	1

	I	II	III	IV	
A					
B					
C					

a. Copy the table and enter on it the total number of *machine-hours* available each week on the different types of machine and the machine-hours required for each quality of product.
b. The cost per unit were estimated as follows:

	I	II	III	IV
A	42	8	9	4
B	14	2	6	7
C	28	4	12	6

Enter the appropriate costs in your table and suggest the least cost solution.
c. Find the total weekly profit provided by your allocation if selling prices are as follows:

	I	II	III	IV
Selling price per unit	56	20	18	10

(Cambridge Local Examinations Syndicate A Level)

B10 At the beginning of 1979, Blowdyke Ltd expects to have 3,000 units of
product X in stock. At the end of that year, this product is to be phased
out, with 1,000 units only left in stock. In each quarter units sent out
should be – 1st 1,000, 2nd 3,000, 3rd 4,000 and 4th 2,000. For management reasons, production is to be evenly distributed over the four quarters. Storage and handling costs per unit are normally £1 for each unit
produced and sent out in the same quarter and £2 if held until the following quarter. Thereafter, each time a unit is held until the next quarter, it
costs a further £2 in storage.

   a. Using a matrix of the form shown below, allocate production and initial stock to despatches and final stock, in order to minimise stockholding costs. Assume that initial stock is all produced in the last
quarter of 1978.

   b. Calculate from the matrix the total stockholding costs arising within
the period from the last day of 1978 to the first day of 1980, showing
that the optimum minimum level can be achieved in more than one
way.

	Initial stock	Production 1979			
		1st quarter	2nd quarter	3rd quarter	4th quarter
1st quarter					
2nd quarter					
3rd quarter					
4th quarter					
Final stock					

(Cambridge Local Examinations Syndicate A Level)

C. Essay Questions

C1   Describe in detail the characteristics of problems to which you can apply the transportation technique.

C2   Describe three different types of problem to which you can apply the transportation technique.

C3   Suppose you had a problem where costs were not strictly linear. Consider the advantages and/or disadvantages of making 'simplifying assumptions' so that the transportation technique may be used.

C4   The transportation technique produces an optimum allocation of resources. Why might a firm *not* necessarily implement this in full?

C5   In lorry routing problems, one often assumes that transport costs are proportional to distance covered. Is this a realistic assumption?

Chapter 17

Simulation

Objectives: *To show how problems in which variability is a major factor may be optimised using simulation techniques.*

Plan of the chapter:

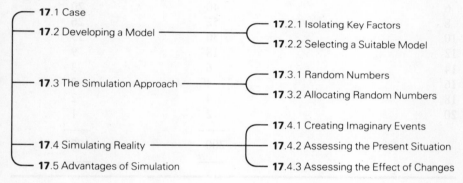

17.1 Case

Merrion's Housing Department has a one-man section which deals with personal visits by tenants. Whilst some such visits are routine (cash payment of rents etc.), some are more involved, dealing with repairs, requests for transfers etc. On occasions, a queue develops and it has been suggested that a second clerk should be recruited to assist. But would two clerks be under-loaded? Are there cheaper and more *effective* solutions? The O.R. team has been asked to look into the problem. The approach needed must take into account the unpredictability of real-live events, particularly those involving queue formation and management (whether of people or objects, as in a warehouse).

17.2 Developing a Model

As given above, the problem needs further investigation before any model can be developed, so the O.R. team first had to gather relevant information.

17.2.1 Isolating Key Factors
Whether or not queues form depends on the interaction of four factors:
a. The pattern of arrivals of 'customers' demanding service.
b. The time taken to deal with each 'customer'.
c. The number of service points available – here, only one.
d. The 'queue discipline' – here, first come, first served, but this would clearly

Customer arrival interval (min)	Frequency	% Frequency
0	4	2
2	12	6
4	28	14
6	40	20
8	52	26
10	30	15
12	18	9
14	6	3
16	4	2
18	4	2
20	2	1
	200	100

Customer service time (min)	Frequency	% Frequency
1	6	3
2	10	5
3	8	4
4	22	11
5	48	24
6	52	26
7	40	20
8	8	4
9	4	2
10	2	1
	200	100

not be the case in a hospital casualty department. (If there are several service points, what rule governs the way in which new arrivals select a queue?)

The team now observed the operation of the section over a period, bearing in mind that there were inevitably seasonal factors at work (e.g. heating and drainage repairs in winter or rent payments being made the day after pay-day). The team recorded two sets of data. Firstly, the time elapsed between successive tenants' arrivals at the section (the '*arrival interval*') and the time taken to deal with each customer (the '*service time*'). For 'normal days', the frequency distributions of the observations are shown opposite.

17.2.2 Selecting a Suitable Model

At first, the O.R. department were tempted to apply statistical techniques to the problem. In particular they were tempted to work entirely with the average figures that were obtained, namely that a customer arrived every 7.84 minutes on average and took an average of 5.45 minutes to be served. It seemed reasonable to argue that since the average service time was less than the average arrival interval, no queue should form.

Whilst this was a superficially attractive analysis the O.R. department had learnt enough about statistical techniques to know that variation was an important consideration in analysis and that somehow this ought to be taken into account when examining the question of number of clerks. After all, if the four customers sharing a zero arrival interval arrived together, and each took nine minutes at the counter, a queue would most certainly form. The necessary ingredient of variation can be obtained using **simulation**. (The alternative name, the **'Monte Carlo' method**, gives an even more graphic idea of its variability.)

17.3 The Simulation Approach

The simulation approach allows the problem solver a great deal of flexibility. As the title suggests, the approach is to imitate what might happen in practice given the data of the problem. Thus we create imaginary tenants, and to each assign an arrival interval and a service time. The picture that we build us is representative of what might happen in practice. To create imaginary tenants, we can use random numbers.

17.3.1 Random Numbers

These are numbers generated by computer, and available in table form, which are random in character. This means that any number has the same probability of occurrence as any other number if a large sample is taken, *provided that the tables are used in a regular manner.*

Figure 17.1 shows an extract from one page of such a table. Note that in a relatively small sample such as this, not all numbers occur, and that some may appear more than once. The distribution in larger samples is, however, random.

20	84	27	38	66	19	60	10	51	20
35	16	74	58	72	79	98	09	47	07
98	82	69	63	23	70	80	88	86	23
94	67	94	34	03	77	89	30	49	51
04	54	32	55	94	82	08	19	20	73
11	25	66	08	79	68	19	37	82	73
00	63	79	77	41	17	06	67	18	33
51	51	54	44	64	13	51	92	10	37
49	72	73	93	29	39	37	94	42	66
77	09	20	05	20	77	47	58	96	05
16	45	77	65	20	11	65	65	56	36
51	63	28	55	12	23	72	99	04	41
64	46	55	58	78	96	52	43	23	05
37	75	41	57	02	14	88	79	97	09
55	36	70	34	66	58	63	90	06	37
99	10	23	74	53	13	59	59	36	71
53	80	84	57	47	60	60	70	69	95
99	29	37	69	30	83	48	05	88	91
21	41	63	90	85	65	07	46	75	43
01	97	45	05	95	88	19	78	14	32

Fig. 17.1: Extract from random number table

If one went from the top left-hand corner, down the first column, up the second, down the third and so on, the numbers occurring would show no bias, provided that a large enough sample was taken. One could have gone in any other manner – diagonally, horizontally, across one and down one – (as long as it was consistently applied) and still obtained no discernible bias.

17.3.2 Allocating Random Numbers

Having obtained distributions of arrival intervals and service times, the next step in the simulation approach is to allocate numbers to these distribution such that the numbers unambiguously represent the frequencies. This is best done using the cumulative percentage frequency for each distribution, as in Fig. 17.2. Note that the number of numbers allocated reflects the frequency of each class interval. So, for the 6 per cent of arrivals having an arrival interval of 2 minutes, there are six numbers allocated: 03, 04, 05, 06, 07, 08.

Customer arrivals

Arrival interval	% Frequency	Cumulative % frequency	Allocated random nos.
0	2	2	01–02
2	6	8	03–08
4	14	22	09–22
6	20	42	23–42
8	26	68	43–68
10	15	83	69–83
12	9	92	84–92
14	3	95	93–95
16	2	97	96–97
18	2	99	98–99
20	1	100	00

Customer service

Service time (min)	% Frequency	Cumulative % frequency	Allocated random nos.
1	3	3	01–03
2	5	8	04–08
3	4	12	09–12
4	11	23	13–23
5	24	47	24–47
6	26	73	48–73
7	20	93	74–93
8	4	97	94–97
9	2	99	98–99
10	1	100	00

Fig. 17.2: Allocated random numbers

17.4 Simulating Reality

17.4.1 Creating Imaginary Events

We can now create (or simulate) 'imaginary customers' by taking random numbers sequentially from the table. Let the first number simulate the customer's arrival interval and the second the same customer's service time. Figure 17.3 shows the random numbers obtained for 20 customers, starting at the top left-hand corner of the table in Fig. 17.1 and working down each column in turn.

Customer No.	Arrival interval random no.	Service time random no.
1	20	35
2	98	94
3	04	11
4	00	51
5	49	77
6	84	16
7	82	67
8	54	25
9	63	51
10	72	09
11	27	74
12	69	94
13	32	66
14	79	54
15	73	20
16	38	58
17	63	34
18	55	08
19	77	44
20	93	05

Fig. 17.3: Twenty simulated customers

The next stage in the simulation is to associate the numbers obtained in Fig. 17.3 with the numbers we allocated to the distributions in Fig. 17.2 earlier. For customer No. 1, the arrival interval random number (20) falls within the range for a 4-minute arrival interval in Fig. 17.2, and the service time number (35) corresponds to a 5-minute service time. Repeating this gives the pattern of arrivals and service shown in Fig. 17.4.

Customer no.	Arrival interval Random no.	Simulated value (min)	Service time Random no.	Simulated value (min)
1	20	4	35	5
2	98	18	94	8
3	04	2	11	3
4	00	20	51	6
5	49	8	77	7
6	84	12	16	4
7	82	10	67	6
8	54	8	25	5
9	63	8	51	6
10	72	10	09	3
11	27	6	74	7
12	69	10	94	8
13	32	6	66	6
14	79	10	54	6
15	73	10	20	4
16	38	6	58	6
17	63	8	34	5
18	55	8	08	2
19	77	10	44	5
20	93	14	05	2

Fig. 17.4: Simulated customer arrival and service times

17.4.2 Assessing the present situation

What the random numbers allow us to do is to investigate what could happen in practice. We have a stream of tenants arriving at the clerk's counter, and we know how long each tenant's problem will take to clear up.

Let us assume that the doors open at 09.00. Customer No. 1 arrives at 09.04, and since there is no queue, goes straight up to the counter, remaining there until 09.09. Customer No. 2 arrives 18 minutes after No. 1, i.e. at 09.22, and can also go straight to the counter, occupying it until 09.30. However, customer No. 3 arrives at 09.24, and so must wait for 6 minutes for the counter to become free.

Figure 17.5 shows the position in the form of a bar chart for the first ten customers.

Clearly on the evidence here, there seems little call for a second clerk. Indeed there may well be a case for investigating just how the time between cus-

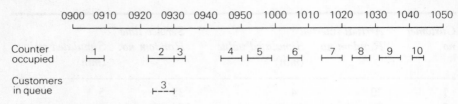

Fig. 17.5: Pattern of simulated customer service for first ten customers

tomers is spent! Even if queues *did* form, we could assess whether an individual's waiting time was 'reasonable', without having to open a second desk.

17.4.3 Assessing the Effect of Changes
If a simulation of the type done above had been done for, say, a supermarket cashier, and had shown that queues were steadily growing larger, one could assess the effect of changed working arrangements. Possible changes might be:

a. A different design of till (for example one that calculates and gives change). This would shorten the service time.
b. Automatic reading of product price labels by the till, thus reducing the service time further.
c. Opening extra tills (in which case one needs to define the new queue discipline. Some banks have a single queue feeding the next free cashier. In others one joins the shortest queue, or the one without the shopkeeper paying in her takings).
d. Having one person to sort and call prices and a second to operate the till.

In each case, small-scale experimentation off the floor of the shop could provide new service time data, and thus assess the effect of each 'improvement' on costs and/or queue lengths.

17.5 Advantages of Simulation

The simulation approach is one of the most favoured of the O.R. approaches. In fact if there was a 'league table' of techniques, the simulation approach would be first if the table was based on number of times the approach was used.

There are a number of reasons for this. One, of course, is the simplicity of the approach. All you have to do is to apply random numbers to the distributions within the problem and generate a set of occurrences that could happen in practice. Second, the approach allows an imitation of the problem that is nearer to reality than some of the other O.R. approaches we have examined.

★ See Question B5

★ Since simulation does not need to have characteristics like linear functions the approach can be applied to virtually any problem without having to make the problem fit into the characteristics that some of the other techniques would require, like the 'linear' requirement of transportation or blending. Third, the simulation approach is very amenable to use with computers. In fact quite a lot of computers provide 'library programs' that allow users to put their problem straight on to the computer by using a standard simulation package. With increasing sophistication, some of the computers now available allow an interaction between the problem solver and the computer itself, allowing one to ask questions of the 'what if' type. The simplicity and flexibility of the approach mean that there is hardly a problem which could not be simulated – stock control, quality control schemes, gambling, operator training, space missions, war games and so on.

★★ Whether one would apply the simulation approach to such problems would depend on the costs and benefits involved. It is reasonably clear that the benefits of using simulation are likely to be greater than those gained from any other approach. But, of course, the costs of using simulation may be greater than using 'simpler' techniques that do not need the use of computers. A balance has always to be struck between the two, as with any problem-solving approach.

★ See Question B6
★★ See Question B8

Work Section

A. Revision Questions

A1 What four factors govern the size of the queue?

A2 Define 'arrival interval' and 'service time'.

A3 What characteristics do random numbers have?

A4 How must one use a table of random numbers?

A5 Why is the cumulative percentage frequency distribution used as the basis for assigning random numbers in simulation?

A6 Does a simulation show what *will* happen in a given situation?

A7 Explain how one converts a random number into a simulated quantity.

A8 Why is simulation seen to be preferable to statistical analyses based on average values only?

A9 How easily can simulation be applied to a problem?

B. Exercises/Case Studies

B1 Apply random numbers to the following distribution and simulate a series of ten machine repair times:

Repair times (hr)	Percentage of observations (%)
$\frac{1}{2}$	40
1	30
$1\frac{1}{2}$	20
2	10

B2 A filling station employs one pump attendant. A survey of 100 customers shows the following arrival and service patterns:

Customers		Attendant	
Arrival interval (min)	Frequency	Service time (min)	Frequency
0.5	2	0.5	12
1.0	6	1.0	21
1.5	10	1.5	36
2.0	25	2.0	19
2.5	20	2.5	7
3.0	14	3.0	5
3.5	10		
4.0	7		
4.5	4		
5.0	2		

a. Simulate the running of the garage for 20 arrivals.
b. What assumptions have you made in your answer to a.?
c. Investigate whether a second attendant is justified.
d. Comment on your results.

B3 Lorries arrive on average once every eight minutes at a loading bay, and the time taken to load is for all practical purposes the same on each occasion, 15 minutes. It would appear that two loading bays should be ample since on average two lorries arrive in 16 minutes, and the two bays can each load one lorry in 15 minutes

Investigate how the present arrangements should work by simulating the arrival of lorries over a two-hour period assuming the following pattern for the interval between the arrival of successive lorries.

Interval between arrival of lorries (min)	Frequency
3	5
4	10
7	45
10	30
13	10

Do you think the number of lorries loaded could be increased significantly?

B4   The probabilities of different numbers of ships arriving at a port on any
day are as follows:

No. of arrivals	Probability
1	0.1
2	0.3
3	0.4
4	0.2

The turn-around time for a ship is four days (including the day of dock-
ing). Thus if a ship arrives on day x and berths on day y, it occupies the
berth until the end of day $(y + 3)$.
There are ten berths altogether, and on 1 June:

One berth is free.
Four berths are occupied by ships which docked on 31 May.
Two berths are occupied by ships which docked on 30 May.
Three berths are occupied by ships which docked on 29 May.

   a. Simulate the arrival and berthing pattern of ships for the month of
June.
   b. Comment on your findings.

B5   A bank branch has two till clerks, one dealing with withdrawals and one
with deposits. Customers arrive at intervals described in the distribution
below:

Arrival interval (min)	Frequency
0	10
1.0	35
2.0	25
3.0	15
4.0	10
5.0	5

On average, half of the customers make deposits and half make withdrawals. It takes 1 minute to serve each type of customer.
   a. Simulate the processing of customers for 20 arrivals, noting the length
of time a customer has to wait and how long clerks are idle.
   b. Investigate whether it would be more efficient for the two counter

clerks to handle both withdrawals and deposits. (In this case, a customer will take 1 minute to serve if he or she requires the same service as the one before, and $1\frac{1}{2}$ minutes if the service required is different.) In the second case assume that there is one queue, and that the customer at the head of the queue goes to whichever clerk is free.

B6 The manager of a photographic retailer is worried by the problem of film sales. The ability to be able to sell film on demand is an important element in the business's marketing policy, so he wants to be able to meet weekly demand in full if at all possible.

He is able to get fresh supplies of film at short notice, an order placed by telephone at the close of business on a Friday will be delivered by post or Securicor before opening on a Monday. (He is not open at weekends.) Taking one film, Ilford FP4, as an example, the weekly sales pattern over the past year has been as follows:

Weekly sales in 19×0
29 28 27 16 21 17 33 19 32 22 36 20 15 31 13 18 25
15 14 13 25 6 9 10 8 10 16 17 11 11 8 23 8 16 14 32
19 8 13 23 12 23 17 20 17 13 28 21 16 26 18.

a. Devise a stock ordering policy which will ensure that he can meet weekly demand for FP4 in full in 95 per cent of weeks in the year. (You will find it useful to make use of the mean and standard deviation of the data.)

b. Simulate six months' worth of sales to see whether your policy works. Assume that the simulation period opens with 60 packs of film in stock.

B7 Critically examine the queueing arrangements in an area known to you, and use simulation to test the effectiveness of alternative ideas which you might suggest.

B8 An importer of machinery and spares receives container loads of orders from overseas, each container being filled with many different orders from one country. At present, the importer's warehouse has two unloading bays and containers on trailers are unhitched for unloading. It takes 24 hr to unload a trailer. The pattern of container arrivals is:

No. of arrivals/day	% Frequency
0	41
1	10
2	22
3	18
4	6
5	3

Each container costs £80 per day to rent, and the firm has considered the possibility of installing extra unloading facilities. A new bay suitable for one extra trailer would cost £10,000 p.a. to operate (including finance charges on construction) whilst a bay designed to cope with two extra containers would cost £18,000 p.a. to operate.

Should the company install extra unloading facilities, and if so, should there be capacity for one or two containers?

C. Essay Questions

C1 Discuss two problems where the use of simulation might be an advantage. In each case, discuss the key factors in the model and the economic and other criteria which one would have to consider in reaching a decision.

C2 Discuss how simulation might improve the effectiveness of education.

Chapter 18

At the End

18.1 A Backward Glance

In working through a text such as this, it is all too easy to concentrate on the sophisticated approach to analysis, and in doing so forget basics. So it is appropriate to end the book with the fundamental questions which are so often forgotten.

Like it or not, the world is becoming a more numerate place, and occupations which, twenty years ago, had little numerate content may now involve the regular use of computers, calculators and so on. Methods of analysis which were the preserve of the research worker are now in common circulation in the general office. Even if you cannot always remember how a particular analysis is done, you need to know that it *can* be done, and then where to turn for help.

Before starting an analysis, always pause to ask what is the purpose of the exercise. What is required and who wants it? Will the intended recipient be able to understand what you have done? When is the information needed? Very accurate information received a week late is virtually useless.

Remember, too, that the exercise may have been done before by someone else. Are there published statistics which will do virtually the same job more quickly or at lower cost? How was the earlier work conducted, and can the methods and results be considered as reliable? If you cannot use others' work, what form of analysis will you use? Which techniques will you employ? Remember that it is preferable to modify a technique to suit the problem than vice versa.

Finally, do remember that your analysis is quite useless unless the ideas it contains are successfully sold. You must communicate your findings to others, who may not share your understanding of the problem or your expertise with numerate tools. Management consultants place great emphasis on the care with which studies are presented to clients. The details of the analysis may not be appreciated, whereas a clear, concise summary using diagrams etc. may well be.

18.2 Digging Deeper

Any introductory text such as this must invariably involve selection. Our aim has been to introduce a range of concepts which even at this modest level can be applied to a wide variety of situations. So the Normal distribution can appear in quality control, stock management, market research, or project planning, as well as scientific research, psychological testing, careers advice and political opinion polls. Only the field of simulation has even wider potential applications.

Furthermore, the ideas introduced differ from more sophisticated techniques only in detail, and not in concept. Master the basic idea of time series analysis, and the refinements needed to manage Sainsbury's stock control programs are more readily mastered. This text should enable you to make more rapid progress when you turn to more specialised works. Quite apart from general texts on quantitative matters, you will find a large selection written on specific fields within the whole. A business school library will contain a wide range of books and papers on operational research, stock control, quality control and the like. Indeed whole books have been written on specific techniques such as simulation or sample surveys. In such works, as with complex crime thrillers, a basic outline of the plot helps you to follow the tale through its twists and turns.

18.3 The Role of the Computer

We have quite deliberately *not* included a section on computers, program writing and so on. In our view, the crucial step in problem solving is recognising that numerate tools can help. The next, more important, stages are framing the problem, the routes to solution, and the form in which the result is presented to the eventual user. This is the field of the systems analyst, and the *real* area of skill in computer applications.

Programming is the process of converting the broad statements of how to crack the problem into the precise 'words' understood by a particular computer. Different machines will require different language, so the programmer is akin to the translator in NATO, who converts the discussion of strategy into the language of the member delegations. Unless you have the breadth of vision to spot where quantitative analysis will help, a computer is a relatively useless box of wires and microcircuits. The best way to learn to use a computer is to get your hands on to a keyboard for an hour or two, with a manual of the language used on your particular machine. That should dispel the notion that computers are omnipotent beasts!

Where the computer scores over a paper-based information society is in the storage capacity and speed of retrieval. In conjunction with suitable program steps, this makes it possible to analyse data in a wide variety of ways in a very short time. Once the data is stored, its potential uses are virtually limitless.

It is becoming increasingly common for this vast reserve of data to be accessible in an interactive manner. This means that the user and the computer's program ask questions of each other in order to provide the necessary information. Thus the designer might move onto a terminal in the drawing office as readily as he reaches for the drawing board. Such use again demands sophisticated program-writing, and hence systems analysis. Relatively unsophisticated users demand increasingly sophisticated analysis teams in the background. And what is their first question? 'What are you trying to achieve?', which is where we came in.

Appendix A

Table of Binomial Coefficients Calculated from $\dfrac{n!}{r!\,(n-r)!}$

n \ r	0	1	2	3	4	5	6	7	8	9	10
1	1	1									
2	1	2	1								
3	1	3	3	1							
4	1	4	6	4	1						
5	1	5	10	10	5	1					
6	1	6	15	20	15	6	1				
7	1	7	21	35	35	21	7	1			
8	1	8	28	56	70	56	28	8	1		
9	1	9	36	84	126	126	84	36	9	1	
10	1	10	45	120	210	252	210	120	45	10	1
11	1	11	55	165	330	462	462	330	165	55	11
12	1	12	66	220	495	792	924	792	495	220	66
13	1	13	78	286	715	1,287	1,716	1,716	1,287	715	286
14	1	14	91	364	1,001	2,002	3,003	3,432	3,003	2,002	1,001
15	1	15	105	455	1,365	3,003	5,005	6,435	6,435	5,005	3,003
16	1	16	120	560	1,820	4,368	8,008	11,440	12,870	11,440	8,008
17	1	17	136	680	2,380	6,188	12,376	19,448	24,310	24,310	19,448
18	1	18	153	816	3,060	8,568	18,564	31,824	43,758	48,620	43,758
19	1	19	171	969	3,876	11,628	27,132	50,399	75,582	92,378	92,378
20	1	20	190	1,140	4,845	15,504	38,760	77,520	125,970	167,960	184,756

Note that for values greater than $n = 10$, not all of the coefficients are shown. In such cases values for $r = 11, 12, 13$ etc. *can* be obtained since the coefficients are symmetrically arranged.

Appendix B

Table of Standard Normal Curve Areas
This table gives areas under the standard Normal distribution for values of z.

z	.00	.01	.02	.03	.04	.05	.06	.07	.08	.09
0.0	.0000	.0040	.0080	.0120	.0160	.0199	.0239	.0279	.0319	.0359
0.1	.0398	.0438	.0478	.0517	.0557	.0596	.0636	.0675	.0714	.0753
0.2	.0793	.0832	.0871	.0910	.0948	.0987	.1026	.1064	.1103	.1141
0.3	.1179	.1217	.1255	.1293	.1331	.1368	.1406	.1443	.1480	.1517
0.4	.1554	.1591	.1628	.1664	.1700	.1736	.1772	.1808	.1844	.1879
0.5	.1915	.1950	.1985	.2019	.2054	.2088	.2123	.2157	.2190	.2224
0.6	.2257	.2291	.2324	.2357	.2389	.2422	.2454	.2486	.2517	.2549
0.7	.2580	.2611	.2642	.2673	.2704	.2734	.2764	.2794	.2823	.2852
0.8	.2881	.2910	.2939	.2967	.2995	.3023	.3051	.3078	.3106	.3133
0.9	.3159	.3186	.3212	.3238	.3264	.3289	.3315	.3340	.3365	.3389
1.0	.3413	.3438	.3461	.3485	.3508	.3531	.3554	3577	.3599	.3621
1.1	.3643	.3665	.3686	.3708	.3729	.3749	.3770	.3790	.3810	.3830
1.2	.3849	.3869	.3888	.3907	.3925	.3944	.3962	.3980	.3997	.4015
1.3	.4032	.4049	.4066	.4082	.4099	.4115	.4131	.4147	.4162	.4177
1.4	.4192	.4207	.4222	.4236	.4251	.4265	.4279	.4292	.4306	.4319
1.5	.4332	.4345	.4357	.4370	.4382	.4394	.4406	.4418	.4429	.4441
1.6	.4452	.4463	.4474	.4484	.4495	.4505	.4515	.4525	.4535	.4545
1.7	.4554	.4564	.4573	.4582	.4591	.4599	.4608	.4616	.4625	.4633
1.8	.4641	.4649	.4656	.4664	.4671	.4678	.4686	.4693	.4699	.4706
1.9	.4713	.4719	.4726	.4732	.4738	.4744	.4750	.4756	.4761	.4767
2.0	.4772	.4778	.4783	.4788	.4793	.4798	.4803	.4808	.4812	.4817
2.1	.4821	.4826	.4830	.4834	.4838	.4842	.4846	.4850	.4854	.4857
2.2	.4861	.4864	.4868	.4871	.4875	.4878	.4881	.4884	.4887	.4890
2.3	.4893	.4896	.4898	.4901	.4904	.4906	.4909	.4911	.4913	.4916
2.4	.4918	.4920	.4922	.4925	.4927	.4929	.4931	.4932	.4934	.4936
2.5	.4938	.4940	.4941	.4943	.4945	.4946	.4948	.4949	.4951	.4952
2.6	.4953	.4955	.4956	.4957	.4959	.4960	.4961	.4962	.4963	.4964
2.7	.4965	.4966	.4967	.4968	.4969	.4970	.4971	.4972	.4973	.4974
2.8	.4974	.4975	.4976	.4977	.4977	.4978	.4979	.4979	.4980	.4981
2.9	.4981	.4982	.4982	.4983	.4984	.4984	.4985	.4985	.4986	.4986
3.0	.4987	.4987	.4987	.4988	.4988	.4989	.4989	.4989	.4990	.4990

Reproduced from *Modern Business Statistics* by J. E. Freund and F. J. Williams (Pitman). After a table in J. Neyman, *First Course in Probability and Statistics* (Holt, Rinehart).